A NEW DIRECTION

A Cognitive-Behavioral Treatment Curriculum

WORKBOOK

Criminal & Addictive Thinking

*Mapping a Life
of Recovery & Freedom
for Chemically Dependent
Criminal Offenders*

**A Collaboration of Chemical Dependency Professionals from
the Minnesota Department of Corrections and the Hazelden Foundation**

 Hazelden Publishing

Hazelden Publishing
Center City, Minnesota 55012-0176
1-800-328-9000
hazelden.org/bookstore

ISBN: 978-1-61649-178-9

Cover design by David Spohn
Interior design by Terri Kinne
Illustrations by Patrice Barton

About Hazelden Publishing

As part of the Hazelden Betty Ford Foundation, Hazelden Publishing offers both cutting-edge educational resources and inspirational books. Our print and digital works help guide individuals in treatment and recovery, and their loved ones. Professionals who work to prevent and treat addiction also turn to Hazelden Publishing for evidence-based curricula, digital content solutions, and videos for use in schools, treatment programs, correctional programs, and electronic health records systems. We also offer training for implementation of our curricula.

Through published and digital works, Hazelden Publishing extends the reach of healing and hope to individuals, families, and communities affected by addiction and related issues.

For more information about Hazelden publications, please call **800-328-9000** or visit us online at **hazelden.org/bookstore**.

CONTENTS

A NEW DIRECTION

A Cognitive-Behavioral Treatment Curriculum

Acknowledgments

Thanks to all who have contributed to this curriculum:

Sheryl Ramstad Hvass
Commissioner, Minnesota Department of Corrections

Peter Bell
Executive Vice President, Hazelden Publishing and Educational Services

James D. Kaul, Ph.D.
Director, TRIAD Chemical Dependency Program
Minnesota Department of Corrections

Will Alexander
Sex Offender/Chemical Dependency Services Unit, Minnesota Department of Corrections

Minnesota Department of Corrections

Sex Offender Treatment Program at Lino Lakes Minnesota Correctional Facility

Robin Goldman, Director
Jim Berg, Program Supervisor
Brian Heinsohn, Corrections Program Therapist
Greg Kraft, Corrections Program Therapist
K. Kaprice Borowski Krebsbach, Corrections Program Therapist
Kevin Nelson, Corrections Program Therapist
Tim Schrupp, Corrections Program Therapist
Pamela Stanchfield, Corrections Program Therapist
Jason Terwey, Corrections Program Therapist
John Vieno, Corrections Program Therapist
Cynthia Woodward, Corrections Program Therapist

TRIAD Chemical Dependency Program at Lino Lakes Minnesota Correctional Facility

Launie Zaffke, Supervisor
Randy Tenge, Supervisor
Carmen Ihlenfeldt, Acting Supervisor
Thomas A. Berner, Corrections Program Therapist
Toni Brezina, Corrections Program Therapist
Jeanie Cooke, Corrections Program Therapist
Ronald J. DeGidio, Corrections Program Therapist
Susan DeGidio, Corrections Program Therapist
Maryann Edgerley, Corrections Program Therapist
Connie Garritsen, Corrections Program Therapist
Gerald Gibcke, Corrections Program Therapist
Anthony Hoheisel, Corrections Program Therapist
Deidra Jones, Corrections Program Therapist
Beth Matchey, Corrections Program Therapist
Jack McGee, Corrections Program Therapist
Jackie Michaelson, Corrections Program Therapist

Hal Palmer, Corrections Program Therapist
Terrance Peach, Corrections Program Therapist
Holly Petersen, Corrections Program Therapist
Linda Rose, Corrections Program Therapist
Kathy Thompson, Corrections Program Therapist
Beverly Welo, Corrections Program Therapist

Reshape Chemical Dependency Program at Saint Cloud Minnesota Correctional Facility

Robert L. Jungbauer, Director
Christine Fortson, Corrections Program Therapist
Tracanne Nelson, Corrections Program Therapist
Jeffrey D. Spies, Corrections Program Therapist

Atlantis Chemical Dependency Program at Stillwater Minnesota Correctional Facility

Bob Reed, Director
Dennis Abitz, Corrections Program Therapist
Bill Burgin, Corrections Program Therapist
Tom Shipp, Corrections Program Therapist

New Dimensions Chemical Dependency Program at Faribault Minnesota Correctional Facility

Michael Coleman, Supervisor
Michele Caron, Corrections Program Therapist

Central Office

Jim Linehan, Corrections Program Therapist

Minnesota Department of Corrections Supervising Agents

Russ Stricker, Correctional Unit Supervisor
Bobbi Chevaliar-Jones, Intensive Supervised Release Agent
William Hafner, Corrections Agent
Gregory Fletcher, 180 Degrees Halfway House

In Addition:

Writers: Corrine Casanova, Deborah Johnson, Stephen Lehman, Joseph M. Moriarity, Paul Schersten.
Designer: Terri Kinne. **Typesetters:** Terri Kinne, Julie Szamocki. **Illustrator:** Patrice Barton.
Prepress: Don Freeman, Kathryn Kjorlien, Rachelle Kuehl, Joan Seim, Tracy Snyder, David Spohn.
Editor: Corrine Casanova. **Copy editors:** Monica Dwyer Abress, Kristal Leebrick, Caryn Pernu.
Proofreaders: Catherine Broberg, Kristal Leebrick. **Marketer:** Michelle Samlaska. **Video production manager:** Alexis Scott.

Special thanks: Any Color Painting Company; Blue Moon Production Company; Eden Re-entry Services; inmates and staff of Lino Lakes, Rush City, and Stillwater Minnesota Correctional Facilities.

Special thanks to Hazelden: Nancy Alliegro, Derrick Crim, Joe Fittipaldi, Carole Kilpela, Nick Motu, Karin Nord, Patricia Owen, Rebecca Post, Teri Ryan, Ann Standing, Sue Thill, and Kris VanHoof-Haines.

We are also indebted to Dr. Stanton E. Samenow, Ph.D., author of *Inside the Criminal Mind*, for his pioneering on criminal thinking.

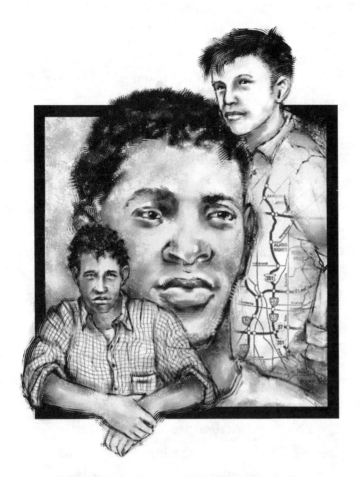

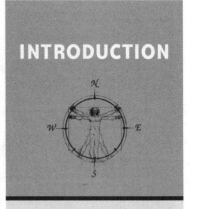
Mapmaking

*Your **best** thinking is what got you here.*

Thinking is how we get around and function in the world. It's what directs us to do one thing rather than another, to go here and not there, to say this and not that. Thinking is how we **interact** with the world.

First, the world provides us with *experiences* that we take in with our senses—sight, hearing, touch, taste, smell, and intuition. Next, we *process* that information—we make sense of it for ourselves—through our thinking. And finally, our thinking shows how we will *respond* to the world—what we will do or say, or not do or say.

This thought process—taking in information, thinking about what it means and how to respond, and then acting upon that thinking—is what sets human beings apart from other animals. While other animals have some kind of thought processes related to survival, reproduction, and avoiding pain, only humans have the ability to think about their thoughts.

As a criminal and an addict, however, you haven't been thinking about your own thoughts very much or very well. In fact, you have been impulsive, selfish, abusive, disconnected from people, and arrogant. You've been behaving like less than the human being you could be. As a result, you are suffering negative consequences.

As one inmate put it to another,

> ## "Man, you just don't get it.
> ## You're **incarcerated.**
> ## You been kicked out of the **world.**"

Look around you. You are lost, and you don't know why. You need to find out why you've been "kicked out of the world." You need a good map to find your way out of this maze. You need to become fully human again.

Interact

Interact means that two or more things act back and forth on each other. Participants in a therapeutic community group interact—they take in information from each other, are changed by it, and give feedback. A healthy person interacts with the world.

Thought Maps

It's still possible for you to change your thinking. Thinking is the tool people use to create a mental map of the outside world: what it is like, where the boundaries are, and where it is safe or dangerous.

We develop our own personal mental map as we are growing up. This information is made up of everything that goes on around us and our responses to it. Our personal mental map consists of all the things we encounter in life—interactions with parents, teachers, neighbors, strangers, authorities, friends, relatives, people we never meet but only hear about, nature, television, stories we read or hear, movies, music, art, history, and other parts of our culture.

Often, we don't even realize when we are adding to our map by learning something new or reinforcing a previous experience. Mental mapmaking happens unconsciously and goes on *constantly.* It is going on right now.

EXERCISE 1 EXERCISE

Using a Map

What are maps for? Imagine a road map, either one someone drew for you or one you would get at a gas station or find in an atlas. Think about what road maps are for and how we use them.

➤ Describe how you would use such a map and why you would need it.

_____

_____

_____

_____

_____

_____

_____

_____

Now imagine that the map you are using is not completely right. It is outdated; things have changed since it was drawn. New roads were built and old ones closed down. Also, the people who drew this map didn't have all the information they needed, or some of the information they had was wrong, or they were sloppy in their work. Because of all this, a few roads and landmarks are labeled incorrectly.

➤ What are some of the possible consequences of following an inaccurate map?

1. _____

_____

2. _____

_____

3. _____

_____

Not all maps are the same.

Figure 1

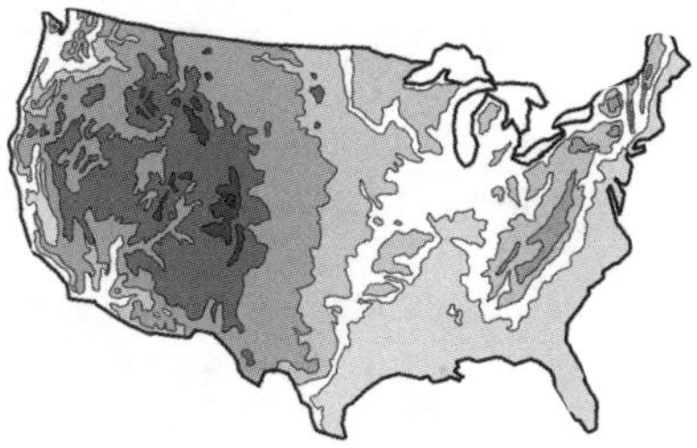

Figure 2

Figure 3

Despite their differences, each of these maps represents the same area of land, which we recognize as the United States. Each map attempts to tell the truth about that land area. Obviously, however, each is very different in the type and quality of information it provides.

➤ What are some differences between the three maps?

_____

_____

_____

_____

_____

_____

_____

_____

_____

Each map represents the land area called the United States, yet each has a different value and purpose. Keep in mind that these maps are not the United States itself; they are *representations* of it. Not only that, as you can see, each map has its limitations and distortions.

These maps are not reality.
Each one is merely a different
representation of reality.

The same is true of your own personal mental map. And just as each of these three maps has flaws and limitations, so does your personal mental map. Even though your inner map has distortions and areas that are incomplete, *it's all you've got.* It gives you direction, shows you where you are located in respect to the rest of the world, and ultimately guides your behavior. It tells you which way to go and shows the different paths you can take to get there. It also indicates what to look out for (landmarks and obstacles) along the way.

Trying to Navigate with Faulty Maps

Thinking, then, is (1) how you map the world and (2) how you get around in it. But here's the catch: *what you think is not always right.*

People are capable of wonderfully creative and useful thoughts. They are also capable of making terrible errors in their thinking. These errors can cause pain, humiliation, guilt and remorse, and loss of freedom. Sometimes your mental map of the world is simply wrong. Instead of bringing you pleasure and safety and abundance, it might instead strand you in quicksand or lead you over a cliff.

With a faulty map, the pathway to paradise can turn out to be the road to ruin.

With an inaccurate map, you can get lost in the world, have one bad experience after another, and get more and more hurt, frustrated, and miserable.

All this is the bad news, and it explains why you are reading this while incarcerated. Your thought map didn't work for you—it led you to where you are right now.

"We cannot solve the problems we have created with the same thinking that created them."

— Albert Einstein

Constructing a New Thought Map

The good news is, you're in charge of your mental map. You can figure out which parts of your old, faulty mental map don't work. Then you can learn how to begin the process of erasing those parts and start creating new, effective maps. Will it take effort? Yes. Can you do it? Yes, you can—*if you make that decision.*

Many, many people in situations similar to yours have done it. This workbook will give you the tools you'll need and teach you how to use them—if you do the work. The therapists and instructors of this program will provide guidance and direction—if you accept what they have to offer. It's your choice.

Drugs, dishonesty, denial—those are the thought maps that got you where you are today: Behind bars. Addicted to alcohol or other drugs. Separated from family, distrustful even of your so-called friends. Angry at the world, angry at society, angry at judges and prosecutors, angry at family, angry at staff, angry at fellow inmates. Maybe even angry at yourself.

This treatment program offers you help in writing a better map. It will teach you how to begin to change *what* you think and *how* you think. Three ideas sum up the workbook's basic approach:

1. Our thinking greatly influences our feelings and our behavior.

2. We can learn to monitor our thinking (to think about our thinking) and change it.

3. Our behavior patterns will change based upon the changes in our thinking patterns.

Keep the following in mind as you move through this workbook. It's an important concept.

There are problems, and there are the ways you choose to handle these problems. They are two different things. What often gets you into trouble isn't always the problems you face but how you respond to them.

Creating new thought maps *will* take effort, but over time you'll see the benefits. Nobody likes change, but change is just a part of being human, and no one can escape it.

Goals of This Workbook

Our previous experience in treating chemically dependent criminal offenders has shown that anyone who makes an honest effort to complete the exercises and practice the concepts can succeed.

The four goals of this criminal and addictive thinking program are to help you

1. learn how to think about your own thinking

2. learn that distorted, extreme thinking leads to distorted, extreme emotions and behavior

3. learn how to identify and stop old criminal and addictive thinking patterns before you act or react

4. replace unsuccessful patterns of thinking with rational choices that will, over time, change those old patterns and lead you to a happier, healthier, more free way of life

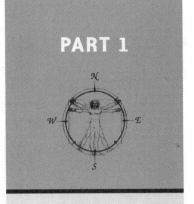

Criminal and
Addiction History

The first step in creating a new thought map is to understand why you *need* a new map. To do that, you must recognize that you are where you are today because of your current map.

You have to identify the problem and take responsibility for it. As a criminal and addictive thinker, you most likely will first respond by saying, "I haven't got a problem. I'm fine."

You may deny that alcohol or other drugs are a problem for you. You may deny that you like the rush of excitement of doing forbidden things. You may even deny the terrible consequences of your criminal lifestyle and addiction, even though you are looking through bars and razor wire.

Addicts and criminals think and behave in many ways when using drugs or committing crime. Some want to fight or argue, some feel sorry for themselves, while some blame others for their problems. Some go off by themselves, abandoning their family and friends. Others act out aggressively. Some criminals and addicts do all of this—and more! We'll learn more about the different types of criminal and addictive thinking patterns in part 3, "Learning to Think about Your Thinking." Changing these patterns will be your map to freedom and sobriety.

> **Changing these patterns will be your map to freedom and sobriety.**

EXERCISE **2** EXERCISE

Your Criminal History

The first step to honesty and recovery is admitting to and taking responsibility for your criminal past. List every crime you've been arrested and convicted for. Write the year of the offense after each listing.

For some of you, this will be a long list. If necessary, complete this exercise in a notebook. List your crimes in order, from your most recent all the way back to your first crime.

➤ Crime   Year

1. _____ _____

2. _____ _____

3. _____ _____

4. _____ _____

5. _____ _____

6. _____ _____

7. _____ _____

8. _____ _____

9. _____ _____

10. _____ _____

➤ How much time have you spent locked up for these
offenses?

_____ years   _____ months

➤ What is the longest time you have spent crime free?

_____ years   _____ months

➤ What crimes did you commit while under the influence of alcohol or other drugs?

_____

_____

_____

_____

_____

➤ What crimes did you commit while trying to get alcohol or other drugs?

_____

_____

_____

_____

_____

➤ Did you ever switch to different types of crimes? (check one)

_____ Yes   _____ No

If so, why did you switch, and when?

_____

_____

➤ Were most of your crimes committed on the spur of the moment, or did you think them through first? For example, did you ever steal just for the thrill of it? Give some examples of how you planned or didn't plan crimes from your own criminal history.

_____

_____

_____

_____

➤ For you, what have been the five worst consequences of your criminal behavior?

1. _____

_____

2. _____

_____

3. _____

_____

4. _____

_____

5. _____

_____

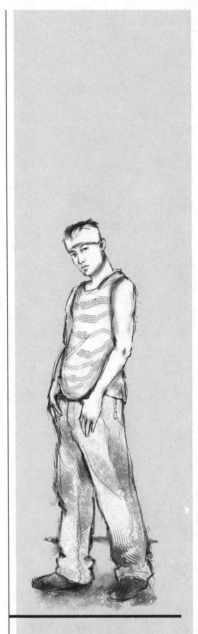

The first step to honesty and recovery is admitting to and taking responsibility for your criminal past.

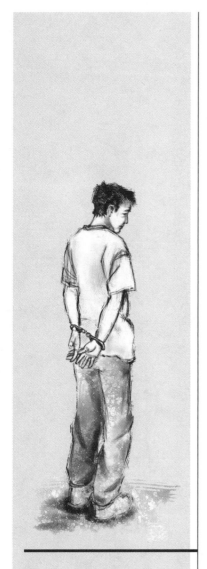

> Give five reasons why criminal behavior and a criminal
> lifestyle seemed attractive to you.

1. _____

_____

_____

2. _____

_____

_____

3. _____

_____

_____

4. _____

_____

_____

5. _____

_____

_____

*What have
been the worst
consequences
of your criminal
behavior?*

Your Addiction History

➤ Just as with your criminal history, the first step to honesty and recovery from your addiction is admitting your chemical history. List every type of drug you have used to get high, as far back as you can remember. After listing each drug, write the year you first used it and the year you most recently used it.

Again, for some of you, this will be a long list. If necessary, complete this exercise in a notebook. **Note:** List each drug only once. Don't list every single time you got high on the drug—just the first and most recent time you used it.

Drug	Year of first use	Year of most recent use
_____	_____	_____
_____	_____	_____
_____	_____	_____
_____	_____	_____
_____	_____	_____
_____	_____	_____
_____	_____	_____
_____	_____	_____
_____	_____	_____

➤ What are your drugs of choice? Just before your most recent arrest, how much did you use of each in a typical week?

Drug   Amount used each week

1. _____   _____

2. _____   _____

3. _____   _____

4. _____   _____

➤ Did you ever have trouble concentrating because you day-dreamed about using alcohol or other drugs? (check one)

_____ Yes   _____ No

If so, how often did this happen? (circle one)

Rarely   Often   Constantly

➤ Did your use of alcohol or other drugs increase or decrease over time? If it increased, how? What time in your life was your use the heaviest?

_____

_____

_____

_____

➤ Give five reasons why using alcohol or other drugs seemed
attractive to you.

1. _____

2. _____

3. _____

4. _____

5. _____

➤ Did you ever move to another neighborhood, city, or state to
escape the consequences of your alcohol or other drug use
or to "get a fresh start"? Explain.

_____

_____

_____

➤ Did you hide your drug of choice? If so, why and from
whom? How did you protect your supply?

_____

_____

_____

Blackout

A *blackout* is when a person under the influence of alcohol or other drugs continues to function but has no memory afterward of what happened. A blackout is not passing out; it is a period of time when you cannot recall what happened.

➤ Have you ever had a ***blackout*** or overdosed taking drugs or drinking? List examples.

_____

_____

_____

_____

_____

_____

➤ List four examples of abuse that you committed while you were high. The types of abuse are physical, emotional, verbal, and sexual.

1. _____

_____

2. _____

_____

3. _____

_____

4. _____

_____

➤ Have you ever felt bad about things you did while you were high? Explain.

_____

_____

_____

➤ List three reasons why you think your addiction is out of control. Examples may include wanting to stop but using anyway, seeking out drugs even though you knew it was dangerous, committing crimes only because you needed to get high, and so on. Describe each incident and how it seemed out of control.

1. _____

   _____

   _____

2. _____

   _____

   _____

3. _____

   _____

   _____

Were most of your crimes committed on the spur of the moment, or did you think them through first?

➤ For you, what have been the five worst consequences of your use of alcohol or other drugs?

1. _____

   _____

2. _____

   _____

3. _____

   _____

4. _____

   _____

5. _____

   _____

➤ Have you ever promised or tried to stop using alcohol or other drugs? Explain.

_____

_____

_____

➤ What is the longest time you have been sober (not used alcohol or other drugs) since you started using?

_____

➤ Why did you try to sober up?

_____

_____

➤ Why did you start using again?

_____

_____

➤ Have you ever been in drug or alcohol treatment before? List each place of treatment the year you entered, and whether you were forced to enter or you entered of your own free will. List your treatments in order, from your most recent back to your first treatment. State whether you completed them.

Treatment place	Year	Forced?	Completed?
_____	_____	_____	_____
_____	_____	_____	_____
_____	_____	_____	_____
_____	_____	_____	_____

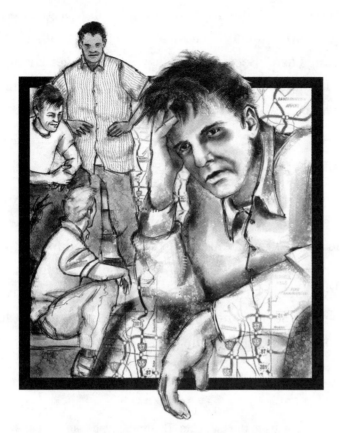

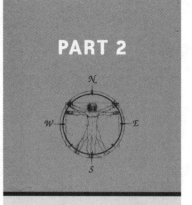

PART 2

Becoming
Aware of Your
Inner Maps

*We look at the world **through** our maps.
We seldom stop to look **at** our maps.*

The first step to changing your thinking is
to become aware of your thinking patterns. In
order to "think about your thinking," you
must first stop and identify your thoughts.
Over time, you will see a pattern.

Keep in mind that we take our thinking for granted—much of it is "automatic" because we believe "that's just the way things are." Because of this, we tend to get thoughts mixed up with feelings, beliefs, and attitudes. To begin to sort it all out, we need to understand how thinking works.

Noticing Your Thoughts

Most thoughts happen in response to some sort of event. The event may be someone bumping into you, the smell of good food, your favorite team scoring a touchdown, or your partner yelling at you. After an event, some thoughts arise right away. Other thoughts may come later, especially if the event is seen as negative. Almost always, some sort of behavior will result from these thoughts. This is how it works:

Figure 4

The event leads to the thoughts. The thoughts cause the behavior.

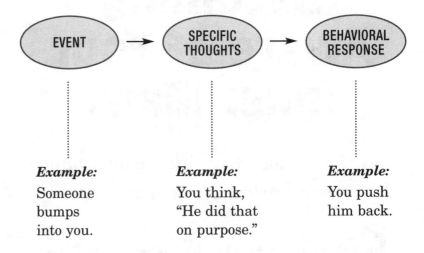

EVENT	SPECIFIC THOUGHTS	BEHAVIORAL RESPONSE
Example: Someone bumps into you.	*Example:* You think, "He did that on purpose."	*Example:* You push him back.

Often, this happens so quickly you don't even notice your thoughts. You may believe the behavior results directly from the event. This is simply not true.

Your behaviors are <u>always</u> the result of your thinking, whether you're fully aware of your thoughts or not.

This is very important: Your behavior never bypasses your brain. The event triggers specific thoughts, which lead to your actions (behaviors).

 EXERCISE **4** EXERCISE

Noticing Thoughts

Imagine that you are in your apartment in a large apartment building. It's 11 at night. You're wide awake and feeling pretty good. You're playing your stereo loud—your favorite CD—and you're really enjoying it. There's a knock at your door. You open it to see a guy standing there with a frown on his face. It's obvious that he's upset.

"Man, could you turn it down? The music is coming right through the walls, and I'm trying to sleep. I've got to work tomorrow."

You think, "Who is this guy to tell me what to do in my own apartment?" You feel the blood rushing to your face, feel the anger starting to build. You pause. Then you let him have it:

"F—— you. This is my place. I pay the rent here. You think I don't work? You're f——ing with the wrong guy, buddy. Get the hell out of here."

As you speak, you lean forward and puff out your chest. Your fingers close into a fist and open and close again. You glare at the man, who has taken a half-step back, stunned. You wait a moment for your words to sink in. You slam the door in his face and go back to your stereo.

You turn the volume up another notch and sit down on your couch. Your good mood is now long gone. You are fuming. Your thoughts continue to spin. You want a drink (or a fix or a joint), and you want it now. You start thinking about where and how to get one.

■

What just happened? Why did it happen? Did it have to happen the way it did?

The details aren't important: It's the thinking and response we're concerned with. It doesn't matter whether you think you would respond like this or not. The point is, many criminals and addicts *would* think and react this way, and the chances are good you might, too. It's fairly predictable because it's part of a thinking pattern common to many criminals and addicts.

This pattern of thinking makes up your personal thought map. As you'll see later, your personal thought map isn't unique. It represents a thinking pattern you share with most other addicts and criminals.

■

What thoughts go through your head when someone confronts you?

➤ What thoughts might be going through your head after the man tells you to turn down your music? List them below.

EXAMPLE:

"Nobody can tell me what to do in my own apartment."

_____

_____

_____

➤ You may have many other thoughts after you slam the door. Imagine yourself in the situation again and list several possible thoughts.

EXAMPLE:

"I'm minding my own business. Why doesn't he mind his?"

_____

_____

_____

 EXERCISE 5 EXERCISE

Reporting Events

➤ The event is the thing that happened that led to the thoughts, feelings, and behavior. Go back and reread the situation described in exercise 4. Describe the event in that situation.

_____

_____

_____

With your group, talk about your report of the event. Did you actually report just the event, or did you give your judgment and feelings about the event? For instance, "I was disrespected" is not an event; it's an *interpretation*, or judgment of an event. Your report of the event should be a simple description of what happened.

Reporting Events and Noticing Thoughts

Now think about an event that actually happened to you either yesterday or today. It doesn't matter whether it made you feel good, bad, or nothing at all. All we're concerned about is learning to notice and clearly identify your thoughts. In writing down the event, just report the facts of what happened. In other words, try to step outside yourself in reporting the event.

➤ What was the event?

_____

_____

_____

➤ What were your thoughts in response to this event?

_____

_____

_____

_____

_____

_____

Noticing Your Feelings

We've learned to identify events. These events lead to thoughts, and thoughts result in behavior. Feelings, or emotions, also result from specific thoughts about the event. How you think affects your feelings.

Figure 5

Feelings also result from thoughts.

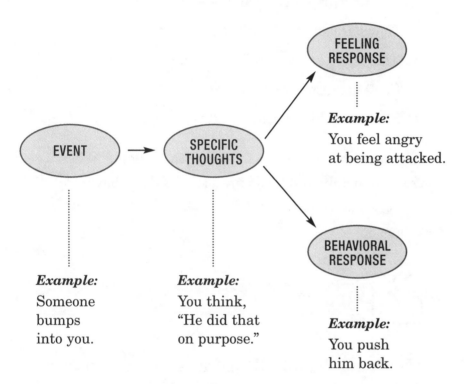

Example:
Someone
bumps
into you.

Example:
You think,
"He did that
on purpose."

Example:
You feel angry
at being attacked.

Example:
You push
him back.

Again, your reaction to an event happens so quickly that you often don't notice your thoughts. Just as the behavior seems to result directly from the event, it may also seem that feelings arise from the event. This is also not true.

Your behaviors and your feelings are the result of your thinking, whether you're fully aware of your thoughts or not.

An event triggers specific thoughts, which lead to both your feelings and your actions (behaviors).

For example, a man who has hit his wife may say, "She made me angry and I just snapped." This suggests that he believes she was responsible for his feelings (anger) and the feelings directly caused the behavior (he "snapped" and became violent). This is not the case. If he looked more closely, he'd find that his thoughts led to the violent behavior. Here are some thoughts he may have had:

- "How dare she talk back to me."
- "This is my house. I'm the man here."
- "She's been on my case all day."
- "She was asking for it."

Emotions do have a role to play with thoughts. When you're emotionally upset, you are more likely to have *a lot* of negative thoughts. These thoughts may lead to negative behaviors.

EXERCISE **7** EXERCISE

Noticing Feeling Responses to Thoughts

What are feelings? To figure it out, let's look at the example of the event in exercise 4, the man at your door telling you to turn down your stereo. Choose one of the thoughts you listed in exercise 4 as a response to that event. Then list three possible feeling responses to that thought.

EXAMPLE:

Specific thought	Possible feeling response
"Nobody tells me what to do in my apartment."	*"I'm angry that the good time I was having got interrupted."*

➤ **Specific thought**

_____

_____

Possible feeling responses

1. _____

_____

2. _____

_____

3. _____

_____

A wide range of feelings could result from the thoughts a person has in response to any event. Some feelings are pleasant or enjoyable ("I feel happy about that"), and some are unpleasant and disturbing ("That makes me feel really angry"). There are also many types of feelings that would fall between those two opposites. In fact, in the English language, there are about two thousand single words, not counting longer phrases or even slang words, that could complete the sentence "I feel _____."

When you're emotionally upset, you are more likely to have a lot of negative thoughts.

One of the first steps in identifying, understanding, and recognizing feelings in yourself and others is learning how to give names to your emotions. The same emotion can have several names depending on whether the feeling is mild or more intense.

Emotion	Mild	Moderate	Extreme
Sad	disappointed	gloomy	devastated
Afraid	nervous	scared	terrified
Desire	wish	want	crave
Disgusted	dislike	contempt	revulsion
Angry	annoyed	indignant	furious
Guilty	regretful	sorry	self-hating
Shamed	embarrassed	unworthy	humiliated

Thinking Patterns

Figure 5 showed how feelings and behaviors result from the specific thoughts that arise from the event. When you have the same types of thoughts over and over, you create *thinking patterns.*

Thinking patterns are habits of thinking and responding that become automatic.

As you repeat these patterns over time, you begin to believe that these thinking patterns are absolute reality: "That's just the way I am," you may tell yourself (and others). But you are wrong. Thinking patterns are not "just the way you are." They are "just the way *you have come to believe you are.*" The problem is, once your thinking responses are automatic, you don't question whether those thoughts are the most effective way to deal with things.

What thoughts do you have when you think about entering a chemical dependency treatment program? Positive thoughts? Chances are, they are not. Very few people have happy associations with mandatory drug or alcohol treatment. It is important to understand, however, that this is not "just the way things are."

The thought "having to complete treatment is bad luck," like every other thought, is a choice.

You could just as easily choose to think that being in treatment is good luck.

Patterns of thinking aren't <u>given</u> to us; they're <u>learned and created</u> by us over time.

These patterns of thought are your map of the world: They decide what the world looks like to you and where you choose to go and what you decide to do, day in and day out. If your map is faulty, you're going to get lost. You're going to experience a lot of conflict with others and society. By following faulty mental maps: (a) you broke the law and ended up with the negative social consequences and (b) felt discontented and miserable a lot of the time. If you follow those faulty maps over and over again, you'll probably end up incarcerated and miserable over and over again—and that's insane.

Insanity is doing the same thing over and over and expecting different results.

Where Are You Going?

➤ When you were a child, you probably didn't tell adults, "I want to be a criminal and an addict when I grow up." What did you want to be when you were younger?

_____

_____

_____

➤ What kind of life do you want to lead? Be realistic—skip the "sitting around the pool of my mansion" fantasy. Try to imagine a real living situation you would like to achieve.

_____

_____

_____

_____

➤ What parts of your personal mental map lead you away from responsible goals?

_____

_____

_____

_____

Changing Your Flawed Thought Map

Your personal thought map may be flawed in three ways:

1. It was created in the first place, and continues to be revised and adapted, based on **thinking distortions.**

2. It is made up of particular habits of thinking called **criminal and addictive thinking patterns.**

3. It is supported by **core beliefs,** basic assumptions you have made about yourself, others, and the world that may be in conflict with the facts.

Thinking distortions aren't about *what* you think, but rather *how* you think. To change your faulty thought map, you are first going to have to begin to understand and change *how you think.*

Criminal and addictive thinking patterns are types of inaccurate thoughts that you have used repeatedly and acted on over the course of your life. They are categories of thoughts that are almost guaranteed to lead you into criminal behavior and drug or alcohol use. Let's take a closer look at these two kinds of thinking patterns.

Criminal thinking patterns are common to all criminals. Not every criminal has every single criminal thinking pattern, but every criminal has *many* and probably *most* of them. Criminal thinking patterns are the ways of thinking that say it is all right for you to violate others or the property of others.

Examples of typical criminal thinking patterns are

- "I found myself in a situation."

- "I'd rather be doing time than be straight like you."

- "I punched him because he had no right to look at me that way."

Criminal thinking patterns are common to all criminals.

Because you are addicted to alcohol or other drugs, your thought map is also filled with *addictive thinking patterns*. Addictive thinking patterns are common to all addicts, though not every addict has every single one. Addictive thinking patterns overlap a great deal with criminal thinking patterns, and the two reinforce and drive each other. Addictive thinking patterns are those ways of thinking that say continuing to use alcohol or other drugs is okay no matter what you have to do to make that happen and no matter what the consequences are to yourself or others.

Examples of typical addictive thinking patterns are

- "I can quit whenever I want."
- "My problem isn't drinking; it's my wife's nagging."
- "Nothing ever works out. I deserve to get high."

Core beliefs are assumptions you have made and accepted as true about yourself, others, and the world. They are the most hidden part of your personal thought map. In a way, core beliefs are like the layers of rocks beneath the surface of the land.

Figure 6

A map doesn't show what the country looks like deep beneath the earth's surface.

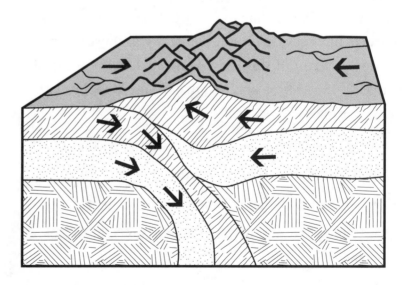

A map of a country will show what the surface of the country looks like: where the roads, rivers, mountains, and so on are located. But beneath the surface are layers of rock and minerals built up and worn down and shifted around over millions of years by oceans, glaciers, volcanoes, earthquakes, wind, and other forces. A map doesn't show what the country looks like deep beneath the earth's surface. Your core beliefs are the deep, unseen part of your mental map. They determine which common thinking distortions (*how* you think) and criminal and addictive thinking patterns (*what* you think) are on your personal thought map.

Here are some examples of core beliefs:

- "I'm not responsible to anybody or anything."
- "Most people are suckers."
- "Life is supposed to be fair."

To build a life free of criminal behavior and alcohol or other drug use, you need to make some choices to fix your personal thought map. You will need to change your map so that it more accurately represents reality and no longer leads you back to incarceration, broken relationships, poor health, and so on.

The first step in fixing your thought map is to identify where it is inaccurate and what you need to change. To do that, you have to be able to think about your thinking.

How to Fill Out a Thinking Report

A Thinking Report is a way for you to practice thinking about your thinking, your core beliefs, and your behavior so you can change them. Thinking about their thinking is a skill that successful people have developed to some degree and that unsuccessful people have developed only slightly or not at all.

Remember, negative thoughts lead to negative behaviors, which lead to negative consequences. Positive, practical thoughts lead to alternative behaviors, which either lead to positive consequences or, at the very least, help to avoid negative consequences.

Thinking Reports are a very important tool in helping you learn how to read your own inner map. They will help you to

1. gradually become *aware* of your own thinking, and

2. learn how to start *thinking* about your own thinking.

Knowing how to think about your own thinking is the most important basic skill you need to create a new, successful thought map.

There are seven main parts to the Thinking Report. They are

1. The **Event**—what exactly happened to begin the chain of thoughts, feelings, and behaviors or potential behaviors.

2. Your **Thoughts**—what popped into your mind when the event occurred.

3. Your **Feelings**—the emotions or other sensations that resulted from your thoughts about the event.

4. Your **Behavior**—your actions in response to the event as directed by your thoughts and reinforced by your feelings.

5. Your **Core Beliefs**—the assumptions you make about the world, others, and yourself.

6. Possible **Alternative Thoughts**—healthier thoughts that are different from your first, automatic thoughts and that could lead to a more positive outcome.

7. Possible **Alternative Behaviors**—what you could do based on your alternative thoughts.

Three remaining sections of the Thinking Report—Thinking Distortions, Thinking Patterns, and Tactics—will be discussed in parts 3 and 4 of this workbook. Leave these sections blank for now.

The Thinking Report looks like this.

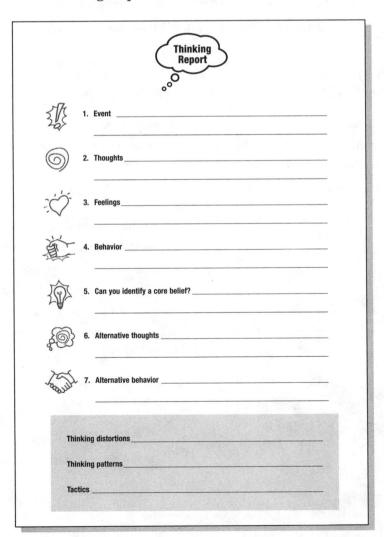

Event

The event is the situation that led to your negative thoughts. The event does not include your responses to the situation —your thoughts, feelings, and behavior regarding what happened. It is simply the thing that happened itself. Your thoughts arise in *response* to the event.

When you fill out a Thinking Report, briefly describe just the facts of what happened—the who, what, when, and where of the situation—as completely as you can. Remember to try to tell the story of the event as someone else who saw the event would describe it.

EXAMPLE:

> *You are sitting down to eat your lunch. A peer walks up to you and says, "You're sitting in my chair. Get out **now**." Then he stares at you.*

This is an accurate report of the event	**These are *not* accurate reports of the event**
I sat down to lunch and this guy tells me I'm in his seat. Then he starts getting loud, telling me to move.	This dude was trying to make me look like a punk during lunch. *(This is a judgment **about** the event.)*
	I told this guy trying to jack my seat at lunch that he had me confused with someone who gave a s—— about what he thinks. *(This is a judgment about and a behavior response to the event.)*

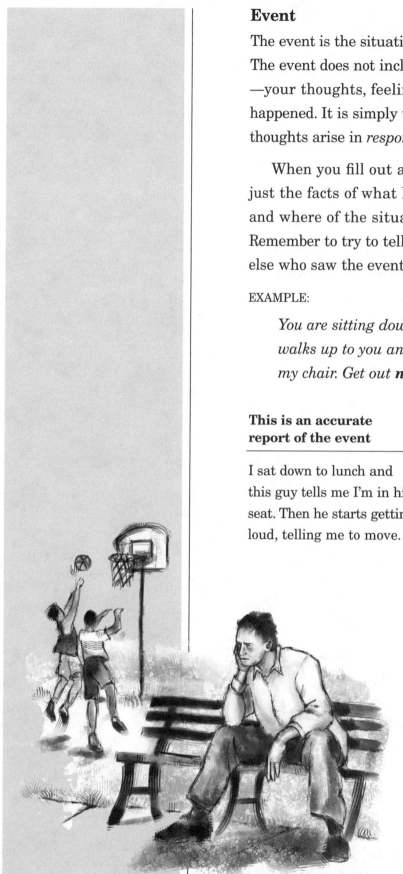

Thoughts

Thoughts are the automatic notions or images you have at the time of the event. To say that these notions, or thoughts, are automatic means they do not arise from a calm process of reasoning but rather just seem to "pop" into your head in the moment.

For this part of the Thinking Report, you list the main thought or thoughts you had at the time of the event.

EXAMPLE:

These are possible (automatic) thoughts

I don't see his name on the bench. What's he trying pull?

Who is this guy? Who's he hanging with?

This dude's disrespecting me, trying to back me down.

F—— you. Who do you think you are?

Feelings

Feelings are the emotions that arise at the time of the event. These emotions may be sad, anxious, angry, pleased, relieved, frightened, or other such feelings. (For more information on feelings, see pages 31–34.) Though these feelings seem to pop up separately from the automatic thoughts you had, in reality, they are the *result* of those thoughts.

In your Thinking Report, list the feelings that you had at the time of the event. Try to determine how intense each feeling was—mild, fairly intense, very intense, or overwhelming.

EXAMPLE:

These are possible feelings

Angry *(very intense)*	Humiliated *(fairly intense)*
Fearful *(intense)*	Nervous *(mild)*

These are *not* feelings

I'll kick his ass.
(This is a thought about how you will respond.)

Others might think I'm a chump if I don't do something.
(This is an automatic thought expressing a fear of humiliation.)

Behavior

The behavior is what you say or do in response to the event. It is the direct result of the negative automatic thoughts you listed. Often the behavior will be a criminal or addictive *tactic*—a strategy you have learned to try to get the results that you think you want. (See part 4, "Learning to Think about Your Behaviors," pages 145–76.) Behavior occurs after the thinking stage. It is *action*. Sometimes it will be something you say; sometimes it will be a physical act; sometimes it will be both.

Describe your behavior in your Thinking Report.

EXAMPLE:

This could be the behavior	This is *not* the behavior
I told him, "Get lost, punk. I'm sitting here now." Then I stood up and stared him down.	I set him straight—let him know who he was messing with. *(This is an interpretation of the behavior, a judgment thought about the behavior after the act had been completed.)*

Core Beliefs

Core beliefs are the basic assumptions we make about the world, others, and ourselves. They make up what we assume to be true about reality and our own self-identity. Core beliefs are formed in childhood as a result of our experiences of the world and are so automatic that we usually aren't even aware of them unless we stop to think carefully.

The main thing to understand about core beliefs is that they are the thoughts behind our thoughts—the things we hold to be true. Our automatic thoughts come out of these beliefs. (Core beliefs are explained more completely on pages 38–39.)

To fill out a Thinking Report, you list one or more core beliefs. Remember, they are the thoughts *behind* the automatic thoughts you've already listed.

EXAMPLE:

These are possible core beliefs	**These are *not* core beliefs**
People will always take advantage of you if you let them, especially in prison.	I really hate that SOB. *(This is a thought showing awareness of a feeling.)*
I'm better than him; I deserve respect.	He must think I'm weak. *(This is an automatic response thought.)*
It's a dog-eat-dog world.	
If I don't watch out for myself, no one will.	

Alternative Thoughts

Alternative thoughts are the thoughts you *could choose* that would challenge your automatic thoughts. Interrupting your automatic negative thoughts gives you a chance to choose a different behavior that you can use over the long haul. Alternative thoughts are a way of mentally stepping out of the thoughts and emotions of the moment and not letting them lead to negative behavior.

Alternative thoughts ask questions such as

- How important is it really?

- How much is it going to cost me in the long term?

- How will I feel afterward if I do what I'm thinking of doing and then get hit with consequences?

Since you really have control over only your own thoughts and behaviors, coming up with alternative thoughts that help you avoid negative consequences is an example of true control—*self*-control.

EXAMPLE:

These are possible alternative thoughts

It's not worth going to seg over or getting kicked out of treatment.

This will blow by if I don't make a show of it.

What do I care where I sit? It's no big deal.

You really have control over only your own thoughts and behaviors.

Alternative Behavior

The alternative behavior is the logical result of the alternative thoughts. An alternative behavior represents a different way of reacting (or not reacting), one that is in your long-term best interests. Alternative behavior is either new behavior, refraining from (*not* doing) some old behavior, or both.

EXAMPLE:

These are possible alternative behaviors

Say nothing and go sit somewhere else.

Tell him calmly, "I was sitting here. There are plenty of seats." And then go back to eating.

If the dude gets more threatening, go sit somewhere else and bring it up in group later.

At the bottom of the Thinking Report form are spaces for "Thinking distortions," "Thinking patterns," and "Tactics." After you've completed parts 3 and 4 of this workbook, you'll be able to fill out those sections, too. For now, just concentrate on the main parts of the Thinking Report.

Remember: The purpose of Thinking Reports is to help you change your thinking and behaviors so that you can

- stay chemical free
- stay crime free
- become a better person in society

Choose situations for Thinking Reports that challenge you, that are difficult, that make you uncomfortable. Often they are the situations that will teach you new ways of thinking and living.

Completing a Thinking Report

➤ Choose an incident that upset or bothered you either today or yesterday and report on what the *event* was, what *thoughts* you had in response to it, and the *feelings* that arose from those thoughts. Report also what you did—your *behavior*—as a result of those thoughts. Then try to figure out the *core belief* you have that may have led you to those thoughts. And finally, try to imagine *alternative thoughts* that could lead to *alternative behaviors* that wouldn't cause problems for you.

When you complete the report, ask your therapist for feedback or discuss the report in group.

Thinking Report

1. Event _____

   _____

2. Thoughts _____

   _____

3. Feelings _____

   _____

4. Behavior _____

   _____

5. Can you identify a core belief? _____

   _____

6. Alternative thoughts _____

   _____

7. Alternative behavior _____

   _____

Thinking distortions _____

Thinking patterns _____

Tactics _____

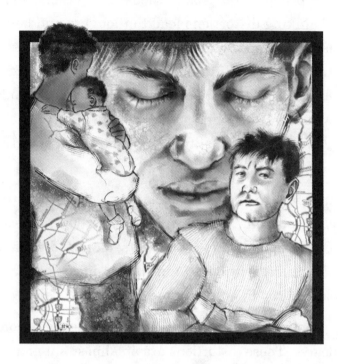

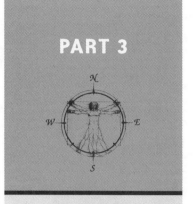
Learning to Think about Your Thinking

Now that you've come to understand how your inner thought maps lead you to act and feel the way you do, it's time to look closer at your thinking habits. How and what you think is what makes up your thought maps, so to change those maps, you need to learn how to change your thinking.

Some Basic Human Thinking Distortions

Thinking distortions are consistently inaccurate and biased ways that people use to look at themselves, others, and the world. Thinking distortions lead to thoughts and beliefs that may sound good on the surface or maybe have some slight truth to them. But thinking distortions misrepresent or distort reality so that your mental map becomes faulty. The result is a self-serving mental map of reality that you use to rationalize and justify your criminal and addictive behavior.

Thinking distortions are about how you think rather than *what* you think. As you will see, distortions in *how* you think can lead to distorted thoughts, distorted behaviors (criminality, irresponsibility), and distressing emotional and psychological conditions (extreme anxiety, rage, depression).

All people, not just criminals, use thinking distortions to some degree. These distortions are an almost automatic way of thinking. They often are not obvious to the person using them. They simply represent "reality" for the person.

Addicts and criminals, however, tend to think mostly or all the time in distorted ways. These distortions help them to justify and rationalize criminal and addictive behavior, and reduce responsibility for actions.

Researchers have identified many thinking distortions that people use. Research also shows that people have personal styles of thinking based on which thinking distortions they find comfortable. Criminal and addictive thinkers consistently overuse certain basic thinking distortions. With practice, you can learn to recognize which distortions you use and replace them with more accurate and effective ways of thinking.

Some of the thinking distortions overlap, and some are harder to understand than others. Don't worry too much about getting them all right the first time—you'll have lots of chances to identify the different thinking distortions in your own thinking. Here are some of the major thinking distortions that criminals and addicts use:

- extreme thinking (all-or-nothing thinking)
- overgeneralization
- personalization
- magnification and minimization
- jumping to conclusions
- selective focus
- concrete thinking
- actor vs. observer bias
- closed thinking
- emotional reasoning

Extreme Thinking (All-or-Nothing Thinking)
Extreme thinking is also called ***all-or-nothing thinking.*** Everything is viewed as either one extreme or the other. Extreme thinking says there is no middle ground. The world is either black or white. There are no shades of gray. Extreme thinking *divides*. Here are some examples:

- "Everybody always . . . "
- "Nobody ever…"
- "Everything I do goes to hell."
- "Nothing ever works out."

Or it can go to the other extreme:

- "I can do no wrong."
- "I always make good choices."
- "My way is always the right way."

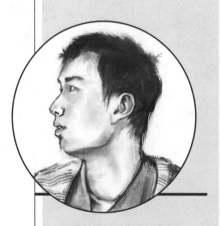

Extreme thinking says there is no middle ground. The world is either black or white.

Extreme thinkers say it's okay to use alcohol or other drugs because "*All* my friends use" and "Since *every*body knows that *every*body steals, why shouldn't I?"

For an extreme thinker, the world looks like figure 7.

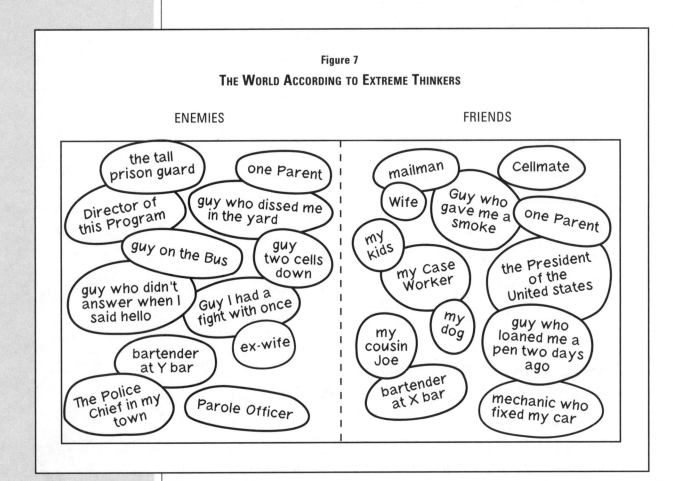

Figure 7
THE WORLD ACCORDING TO EXTREME THINKERS

Extreme thinking *distorts* the way you see the world. In figure 7, all people are either enemies or friends. Extreme thinkers place everyone they meet into one of the two boxes. The result: Once someone is placed in the "enemies" box, it's very hard to move that person to the "friends" box. On the other hand, it's easy to move someone from the "friends" box to the "enemies" box. Over time, the "enemies" box starts to get really crowded, and the "friends" box empties out. (See figure 8.)

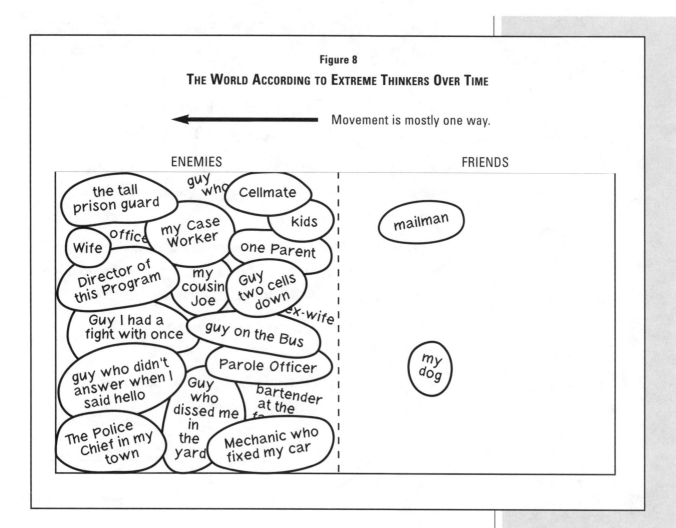

Figure 8

THE WORLD ACCORDING TO EXTREME THINKERS OVER TIME

← Movement is mostly one way.

ENEMIES FRIENDS

the tall prison guard · guy who · Cellmate · kids · Wife · office · my Case Worker · one Parent · Director of this Program · my cousin Joe · Guy two cells down · ex-wife · Guy I had a fight with once · guy on the Bus · guy who didn't answer when I said hello · Parole Officer · Guy who dissed me in the yard · bartender at the · The Police Chief in my town · Mechanic who fixed my car

mailman

my dog

In truth, very few people are truly enemies or truly friends. Most people you come in contact with fit into neither category. Instead, they are in a large, neutral middle category of neither friend nor enemy.

Unfortunately, extreme thinking about the world, ourselves, and others (good/bad, safe/not safe, enemy/ friend, trust/don't trust) leads us to extreme feelings and behaviors. We trust people until the first time they let us down, and then we hate them. We are successes or failures, heroes or zeroes. The world is either fair or not fair. We get angry, even abusive with people, or maybe feel hopelessly depressed about things. The result is a mental map that is so distorted, so limiting, that it operates almost like a personal mental prison, confining you to a very restricted vision of life.

Examples of Extreme
(All-or-Nothing) Thinking

➤ List three examples of extreme thinking that relate to being chemically dependent, about other people, and about criminal behavior.

EXAMPLE: "Unless you are homeless, half-deranged, and sleeping in the gutter, you're not really an addict or alcoholic." (about alcohol or other drugs)

EXAMPLE: "You either respect me or you don't." (about others)

EXAMPLE: "Everybody steals; I just got caught." (about criminal behavior)

1. _____

   _____

2. _____

   _____

3. _____

   _____

*Unfortunately, extreme thinking about
the world, ourselves, and others
leads us to extreme feelings and behaviors.*

Overgeneralization

Overgeneralization is a thinking distortion that says because something happened once or twice, it must always be true. Overgeneralization is the basis for a lot of our problems, including *prejudice* of every kind.

Overgeneralizing thinkers tend to believe that if one person lies to them, then "You can't trust nobody." Overgeneralizing thinkers take a single or isolated event and turn it into a law of the universe: "That's just the way things are," they tell themselves. "Everybody lies." "Everybody steals." "All [those people] are [like that]—I know because I've met some of them." Overgeneralizing thinkers rarely question these distortions. In their minds, it's just "reality."

Prejudice

Prejudice is a negative judgment or opinion of something or someone that is already decided beforehand and is not based on evidence.

 EXERCISE 11 EXERCISE

Examples of Overgeneralization

➤ List some examples of overgeneralization that you have thought, said, or heard about other people, about the world, about chemical use, and about criminal behavior.

EXAMPLE: "Everybody is out for themselves." (about others)

EXAMPLE: "The world should be fair." (about the world)

EXAMPLE: "Everybody I know uses." (about alcohol or other drug use)

EXAMPLE: "Everybody steals." (about criminal behavior)

1. _____

   _____

2. _____

   _____

3. _____

   _____

4. _____

   _____

◼

Personalization

Personalization is a thinking distortion that says everything that happens around you is always all about you. Personalization makes all events somehow related to your life, even when there is no real connection. You think other people's actions and reactions are directed specifically at you every time. Even if others *don't* do something, you think that says something about you, too. Either way, it's all about *you*.

You may think an officer disrespects you if he doesn't respond to your request immediately. You believe it must be because he dislikes you. It doesn't occur to you that maybe it has nothing to do with you at all. You think rules are changed just "to get you to go off" or that your family doesn't answer the phone because they don't care about you (otherwise they'd sit around all day waiting for you to call, right?). You think the parole officer just had it out for you, and that's why he made you take all those urine analyses.

Examples of Personalization

➤ Give two examples of recent events that you personalized—events you thought were all about you but probably weren't. What went through your mind at the time of each event?

1. _____

   _____

   _____

2. _____

   _____

   _____

■

Magnification and Minimization

Sometimes you can magnify or minimize the importance of some event to the point of distorting it. Either you take the event out of context and blow it out of proportion or you play down the event's impact or significance. This is usually done to explain or justify your actions (or inactions) and to excuse the results of your behavior. Magnifying or minimizing tells only *part* of the truth. ***Magnification*** and ***minimization*** are distorted ways of thinking about the world, yourself, and others.

Here are some examples of magnification:

• "I'm late for work, so screw it, I'm not going."

- Automatically believing that something negative said to you is a personal attack.
- "I've been through a lot, so who can blame me for what I did?"

Here are some examples of minimization:

- "It wasn't that bad."
- "My using only hurts me."
- "I caught a case."
- "Anybody can get a DUI."

When you blow things out of proportion, a minor confrontation becomes a major threat. When you make something seem worse than it really is, you respond strongly to everything related to it. When you minimize, you may try to dismiss the results of serious behavior, to convince yourself and others that it's no big deal.

EXERCISE **13** EXERCISE

Examples of Magnification and Minimization

➤ Give an example of an area in your life that you tend to magnify (blow out of proportion).

_____

_____

➤ Give an example of an area in your life that you tend to minimize (dismiss as less important than it is).

_____

_____

Jumping to Conclusions

When you are *jumping to conclusions,* you think you know where things are headed and make a snap decision with little or no evidence. You behave as if you are

- a mind reader—you instantly assume you know the reasons someone is reacting toward you in a certain way, or

- a fortune-teller—you predict or anticipate how things will turn out without waiting for the evidence.

Either way, you don't wait around for the facts, because you have already reached your conclusion.

 EXERCISE 14 EXERCISE

Examples of Jumping to Conclusions

➤ Briefly describe two times when you jumped to conclusions and were wrong.

1. _____

_____

_____

_____

2. _____

_____

_____

_____

Sometimes you can magnify or minimize the importance of some event to the point of distorting it.

Selective Focus

Selective focus is a thinking distortion that means you pick and choose certain parts of an event or situation and focus only on those. What you focus on may be something good or bad. If some facts don't support what you already believe, you block them out. As a criminal and addictive thinker, you are probably an expert at this. You try to control the focus so you can justify your behavior.

For example, depressed people focus only on the negative. They don't ignore the good; they simply don't hear or see it. When you are looking at the criminal complaint against you, for example, you focus on the one or two small errors in the report, rather than the majority of the complaint that is true. Or during a disagreement with staff, you focus only on the one thing they said that you did not like.

EXERCISE **15** EXERCISE

Examples of Selective Focus

In a group discussion, an inmate was receiving feedback from his peers on his progress in treatment. Several members of the group told him they thought he was doing better. They said he was making progress completing his assignments, doing his unit job, and paying closer attention in group. But he still wasn't willing, they said, to talk about his crime or his addiction in group. Later, a peer asked him how things went in group. The inmate said, "They all kept attacking me for not telling them about my crime."

When this situation occurred another time, the participant's response was just the opposite. He heard none of the criticism and reported, "They all told me I was doing well."

➤ Give an example of when you focused on only one part of a situation.

_____

_____

_____

■

Concrete Thinking

With ***concrete thinking,*** you focus on the specifics of an event or situation, but you don't get the message behind the situation. You take things literally, at face value, and have trouble ***generalizing*** from one event to the next. Because you treat each learning event as unique and disconnected, you fail to learn the general rules behind them. That's why you have trouble learning from your mistakes.

Concrete thinking is almost the opposite of overgeneralization—it's *under*generalization. For example, if you get a ticket for running a stop sign, you decide not to run that particular stop sign again. But you continue to run *other* stop signs. If you are told to stop using drugs, you use only alcohol because, in your mind, alcohol is not a drug.

Because you can't generalize from one situation to another, you don't learn from past experiences. You also don't think far enough ahead to see the outcome of your behavior. That's why you repeat the same self-defeating behavior. One definition of insanity is doing the same thing over and over and expecting different results.

Generalizing

Generalizing is the mental process of figuring out the common aspects of different events or things and then being able to draw accurate conclusions from them.

Example of Concrete Thinking

➤ Give an example of something in your life that fits the definition of *insanity* given on page 63, or when you failed to think things through and ended up doing something really stupid. (By the way, being able to admit this is the first step to changing.)

_____

_____

_____

_____

Actor vs. Observer Bias

Actor vs. observer bias is a tough thinking distortion to understand, but it's one that all people can relate to.

As humans, we tend to justify our negative behavior and blame other people or events when things go wrong. We often overlook how our attitudes and actions contributed to the situation. This distortion means that when you are an *actor* in a situation, you tend to focus only on the situation outside of you.

You forget that you

- pick and choose the situations you are in, at least in part,

- are a *part* of situations you are in, and

- have choices about how you deal with each situation.

When you simply *observe* a situation that you are not a part of, you are able to look at both the actor(s) *and* the situation. Ever see two guys get into a fight and then listen to their stories later? Each one blames the other for being a jerk. Neither one sees the part he played in the conflict.

If *you* were in the fight, you may justify your behavior by saying things like, "He was asking for it," "I had to protect myself," or "I found myself in a situation . . ." as if you weren't there and had nothing to do with your own behavior! You forget that you have at least *some* control over the situations you "find" yourself in.

Most of the time you have a lot of control.

Another example of actor vs. observer bias is when you are arrested, you say you "caught a case," like it was some kind of cold. "I caught a case" makes it seem as if you didn't have anything to do with the fact that you decided to go into the convenience store with a gun to rob it, and it didn't go down as planned. This distortion makes you think *you* were the victim; you just "found" yourself in a bad situation.

This thinking distortion leads you to think that you have little or no control over the situations you are in, and so you have few choices. Because you think others are responsible for the situation, you see yourself as the blameless victim. If you're the victim, any negative consequences or outcomes aren't on you.

Examples of Actor vs. Observer Bias

➤ Give a recent example of when the words "I found myself [doing something]" came out of your mouth.

_____

_____

_____

➤ What control did you have in picking the situation? If you think it was completely unavoidable, explain why.

_____

_____

_____

Don't forget that you have at least some control over the situations you "find" yourself in.

Closed Thinking

Closed thinking means not listening to or trusting new information. When your thinking is closed, no one can convince you of anything more than you already "know." You lack self-awareness and aren't open to any new way of looking at things or doing things.

You argue that you're not open to new thinking or new behavior because it's brainwashing and "that's not the real you." You think you have to be true to yourself, right? Who cares if it means life in prison on the installment plan, hepatitis, or even AIDS? You gotta be you. You don't listen to new ideas because no one has anything to tell you anyway.

What you call "brainwashing" the rest of the world calls education and personal growth. What you call "being true to yourself" the rest of the world calls willful ignorance.

EXERCISE 18 EXERCISE

Example of Closed Thinking

➤ Describe a time when you were absolutely closed-minded about something, when you weren't going to listen to anything anybody had to say and were going to do things your own way.

_____

_____

_____

_____

■

Emotional Reasoning

In *emotional reasoning,* feelings are facts. Your feelings are the ultimate guide to how you think about things and what you do. You react according to what you *feel,* basing your actions on emotions instead of on what you *think.* In fact, you may not even be able to see the difference between the two.

What gets lost with emotional reasoning are the thoughts that created the feelings in the first place. You have buried those thoughts and come to believe that your emotions just reflect the way things are. If it feels bad, then you shouldn't have to do it. If it makes you feel good or "right," then you're entitled to do it. When you *feel* like doing something, then you *will* do it. If you don't feel comfortable with something, then you think you shouldn't have to do it.

For example, you may complain that part of treatment is boring, so you decide you shouldn't have to put up with it. Or you say, "There's too much pressure in here. I can't change all at once," so you quit.

You also say "I feel" when you are really talking about what you're thinking: "I *feel* like I'm being treated unfairly" rather than "I *think* I am being treated unfairly." That type of emotional reasoning is an attempt to put the problem on others who have "created" these emotions in you—and it takes you off the hook for what you think.

EXERCISE **19** EXERCISE

Examples of Emotional Reasoning

➤ Give two examples of making decisions based upon your emotions or feelings instead of taking time to think things through more carefully.

1. _____

   _____

   _____

2. _____

   _____

   _____

In emotional reasoning, feelings are facts. Your feelings are the ultimate guide to how you think about things and what you do.

One More Look at Thinking Distortions

As humans, we all use some of these thinking distortions to a degree. As a criminal and addictive thinker, however, you tend to use them to an extreme, even when doing so leads to serious consequences. You don't fully think things through or think far enough ahead.

You probably noticed that some of these thinking distortions are similar and overlap each other. You can use several at the same time. While thinking distortions may help you deal with your criminal and addict "accountability problem" by helping you justify your behavior, they really lead you to trouble. (Remember: Distorted thinking leads to distorted thoughts, which lead to extreme behavior.) By not taking responsibility for your behavior, you don't have to change—you just hope you'll get lucky or that bad situations won't "find" you again. By learning to identify and challenge these distortions, you begin to take responsibility for your behavior and to change your way of thinking. While you probably can't ever remove these distortions completely, you can, over time, develop tools to deal with them.

Consider how these thinking distortions have created problems in your life—for yourself and for others. Your distorted views of yourself, others, and the world have negatively affected your relationships with others, contributed to your alcohol and drug use, and led to your incarceration.

Now you are ready to start identifying the thinking distortions you use and adding them to your Thinking Reports. You can also begin imagining new, alternative behaviors—different ways of responding to the situation—that would be more effective and could help keep you out of trouble. Complete the "thinking distortions" part of the Thinking Report on page 49 of part 2.

Criminal and Addictive Thinking Patterns

Thinking distortions are about *how* you think; criminal and addictive thinking patterns are more about *what* you think. Thinking patterns are habits of thought—types of thoughts a person uses so often that they just seem to come naturally.

As a criminal and an addict, you have developed both criminal and addictive thinking patterns. These thinking patterns aren't all the thoughts you have, but they do dominate your thinking. This leads to trouble.

The good news is, you can change your patterns of thinking with a little help and a lot of effort.

This workbook and your therapists will provide the help; *you* have to supply the effort. No one can do it for you.

We have identified nine criminal thinking patterns and nine addictive thinking patterns. You will notice that some criminal and addictive thinking patterns are very similar or even the same. That's because criminality and addiction are both, to a large degree, *thinking* problems before they become *behavior* problems.

The criminal and addictive thinking patterns are listed on the table on the next page.

As you can see, the two groups of thinking patterns are very similar. Because of this, you can work on them together. Your efforts to change one will reinforce your work on the other. The only catch is, you have to accept that you must recover from both criminality *and* addiction— you can't pick one and leave the other.

Criminal Thinking Patterns	Addictive Thinking Patterns
• victim stance	• self-pity stance
• "good person" stance	• "good person" stance
• "unique person" stance	• "unique person" stance
• fear of exposure	• fear of exposure
• lack-of-time perspective	• lack-of-time perspective
• selective effort	• selective effort
• use of power to control	• use of deceit to control
• seek excitement first	• seek pleasure first
• ownership stance	• ownership stance

Criminal Thinking Patterns

Studies have shown that the decision to commit most criminal offenses occurs within ten minutes of the crime itself. That is, while criminals may think about committing crime for a long time without acting, they decide to act on the spur of the moment. *Criminal thinking patterns* are what allow the criminal to indulge in thoughts of crime and then suddenly act on those thoughts. Criminal thinking patterns are not exclusive to criminals.

Noncriminals may also have thoughts from time to time that fit in one or more of the categories of criminal thinking patterns. The difference is they don't act on them. Criminals use criminal thinking patterns more frequently and across the entire range of their life situations. And criminals act on those thoughts.

Criminal Thinking Patterns

Criminal thinking patterns are the types of thoughts that say it is okay to violate others or the property of others.

You will notice that some of the criminal thinking patterns listed on page 71 are called "stances." A stance is a position you take to show yourself to the world. It is like an image or a pose. These poses are for the benefit of others, to make others see you as you want to be seen. Stances do not come from inside you. They are like masks or costumes. They are essentially fake. As a criminal thinker, you adopt a stance out of defensiveness or desperation. You fear that without your stances, you're really a nothing. You "put on" the front or mask and assume the role of victim, good person, unique person, or owner of whatever you want. Or you may truly believe that you and you alone are unique and powerful, entitled to get whatever you want.

You will learn to recognize these patterns in your thinking and realize that there is a way out after all. You will recognize and challenge your criminal thinking patterns.

Victim Stance

The first criminal thinking pattern is ***victim stance.*** In victim-stance thinking, you view yourself as a victim first. It doesn't matter what you have done to victimize others. The victim stance is a common way to defend yourself when you are held accountable for your behavior. The victim stance allows you to blame others for the situations you usually have created for yourself. You make many excuses and point the finger at others, claiming you were the one who was really wronged. And because you think you were wronged, you think your behavior is justified. Victim-stance thinking helps you gain the sympathy of the person who is confronting you or puts the focus onto that person or someone else—anything to take the heat off yourself.

Again, victim-stance thinking is used to justify your behavior to yourself and to others who hold you accountable. You blame just about anyone or anything for your crime except yourself—even though *you're the one who committed the crime.* "Someone else" was stupid. "Someone else" snitched you out. "Bad luck" got you arrested. "Fate" was against you. "Society" set you up to fail. All of it is just a way of saying, "It's not my fault."

 EXERCISE 20 EXERCISE

Excuse Making

As a criminal thinker, you make excuses for everything. Whenever you are held accountable for being irresponsible or for committing criminal acts, you make excuses to justify your behavior. Making excuses is just another way of trying to convince yourself and others that you're the victim, that it's not your fault. Here are some examples of common criminal thinking excuses:

- "I broke in because I needed the money. People should expect that when they pay us so little."

- "Everyone does it."

- "That purse was just sitting in the booth. I didn't steal it; I found it."

➤ Give three excuses you use for committing crimes.

1. _____

_____

2. _____

_____

3. _____

_____

Correcting Victim-Stance Thinking

A victim-stance thinker needs to learn four new things to change:

- Accept your role in creating the situation. You have to recognize the choices you made and the criminal and addictive thinking patterns you relied on that led you to your incarceration. You must begin to see how your choices and thinking patterns affected everything you did that was irresponsible, not just the crime you were convicted of.

- Become aware of others who grew up in similar conditions of disadvantage and unfairness yet did not develop criminal thinking patterns. They made choices not to violate others or the property of others. Life is not always fair. Some people have it tougher than others, but there is always someone who had it worse than you did who chose to live responsibly. *It's a choice.*

- Realize that you are incarcerated because you are, in fact, the *victimizer,* not the *victim.*

- Understand that thinking of yourself as a victim and presenting yourself to the world as a victim is a huge barrier to developing a responsible lifestyle. The only thing you (or anyone) can ever truly control is your own thinking and behavior. It is *your* responsibility to learn to do just that.

The only thing you (or anyone) can ever truly control is your own thinking and behavior.

"Good Person" Stance

The second criminal thinking pattern is the **"good person" stance.** When you adopt this thinking, you consider yourself to be a good person, no matter what. You work hard to present that image to others. In fact, you may not only consider yourself a good person, you may think you're better than others! You probably don't think you're a criminal thinker at all. But you are.

Here are several examples of "good person" stance thinking:

- "I'm a good person. Look, I help my grandmother with the groceries all the time."

- "There's nothing wrong with my behavior. All I did was sell a little dope, provide a service for my customers."

As a criminal thinker, you use four main strategies to create and maintain the illusion that you are essentially a good person. These strategies are

- sentimentality
- selective memory
- excuses and rationalizations
- false comparisons and self-serving definitions

Sentimentality

Sentimentality involves viewing your motives for committing a crime as always "good" on some level. You can then think you are essentially a "good person," despite your crimes. This is a distorted view to justify a criminal action in your mind or to avoid feeling bad about what you've done. As a sentimental criminal thinker, you might

- rob a bank and then give $20 to a homeless person on the street (you'll think you're a good person for the good deed you did)

You probably don't think you're a criminal thinker at all. But you are.

- make sure to tell everyone how you used some of your drug profits to help out family and friends

This sentimental view of yourself tricks you into believing you're a good person, even though

- The $20 you gave the homeless person wasn't really yours to give away.

- There are always strings attached when you help out family and friends. You expect the people you help to return the favor many times over down the road.

Your sentimentality is often contradicted by your criminal behavior. You may help an old lady across the street but rob an older couple later in the evening. Your good feelings one moment toward old people (or animals, kids, your mother, poor people, religion, and so on) are separated from other, criminal parts of your personality and life.

Selective Memory

As a criminal thinker, you tend to recall only the positive actions you've taken and not the negative ones. This "good person" stance strategy is called selective memory. While you may remember every drug-profit dollar you ever gave to friends and family, you conveniently forget about the guy who overdosed on the smack you sold. The "good person" stance thinker who is using selective memory will

Remember this	but will not disclose this
I gave my girlfriend money for a new coat three months ago. ⟶	I steal from her purse whenever she's not looking.
My conviction is for robbery. ⟶	I also committed domestic abuse but was never prosecuted.

Excuses and Rationalizations

Criminal thinkers often make excuses and try to minimize the harm they have done to others, which is another "good person" stance strategy. For example:

The excuse or rationalization	The bigger picture
Insurance will pay for it.	The victim's insurance rates will go up, or the person's policy will be canceled, and everyone else's rates will rise, too. Plus, I violated the victim's sense of safety, which may take years to heal.
I only took money. I never killed anybody.	The crimes I didn't commit don't magically make the crimes I did commit somehow okay.

False Comparisons and Self-Serving Definitions

As a criminal thinker who uses the "good person" stance, you will try to make yourself look good by continually pointing out that someone else is "worse" than you. The criminal hierarchy found in all prisons is an example of the delusion that some crimes are somehow "better" than other crimes. It's another way of lying to yourself and others about the reality of your behavior.

The "good person" stance lie	The truth
I sell drugs as a service to others.	I sell drugs to get what I want at the expense of others.
Murderers are better than rapists.	Both have committed a violation of the body and soul of another person.

Correcting "Good Person" Stance Thinking

To correct "good person" stance thinking, you need to learn three things:

- Your sentimental goodwill toward others is not consistent. If you want to truly become a good person, someone who helps others, you must do *no* harm to others at any time.

- Put yourself in the other person's shoes. Learn to look at things from the other person's point of view, particularly your victim's. Fully understand that you affect many people with your behavior.

- Your character is determined by the sum total of what you do and don't do, not just by isolated incidents. You are responsible for *everything* you do and don't do.

EXERCISE 21 EXERCISE

I Am Everything I Do

Your character is determined by *everything* you do and think. It is not based on an isolated event. The good you do does not erase the bad—both are true about you. To stop using the "good person" stance, you need to start seeing the whole picture of yourself.

➤ Make a "balance sheet" of your life. On one side, list the good things you have done. On the other, list the harm that you have done. Think about the whole picture of your life. Remember, you were not arrested for the good things you do.

The good I have done	The harm I have caused
1. _____	1. _____
_____	_____
2. _____	2. _____
_____	_____
3. _____	3. _____
_____	_____
4. _____	4. _____
_____	_____

"Unique Person" Stance

The third criminal thinking pattern is called the **"unique person" stance.** When you take a "unique person" stance, you are saying some or all of the following things:

- "I am a loner; I don't need anybody."

- "The [gang, city, 'hood] I came from is not like yours. I'm different—I'm a player."

- "I'm not willing to reveal too much about myself. I need to maintain my secrets."

- "The more I know that others don't, the better. I'm not about to share any kind of information."

- "I won't get caught because I'm too smart."

- "No one has ever gone through what I've gone through, so no one could ever understand me."

When you are in the "unique person" stance, you are vague, deceptive, and untruthful. You lie outright to confuse and mislead others. You withhold key information that could help solve a problem.

You will also be super-optimistic. Super-optimism is an unrealistic expectation that just because you think things should be a certain way, then that's the way they'll be. You commit crimes because you never think you'll get caught.

You believe that if you think it, then it must be that way.

Perfectionism is another characteristic of "unique person" stance thinking. This means you expect yourself to do everything perfectly right away, without practice or failure. You won't try things that don't come easily or that you fear you won't be the best at. Eventually, you stop trying to do anything worthwhile because doing so risks failure. That would mean you're not unique, special, number one.

All this is true *even though you have a long list of failures in your history.* Not only that, it is a big reason *why* you have so many failures. No one can succeed at anything worthwhile by trying it only once.

It's also probably true that you think you're special even in treatment. You think that your criminality is different or that because you're unique, your chemical use is an excuse—it means your behavior isn't truly criminal. And now that you've decided to change, you think, *Presto! You've changed.* Just like that. You think that you now understand everything and don't have to do any real change work.

Like the other criminal thinking patterns, "unique person" stance is just another way that you justify not being responsible or productive.

Correcting "Unique Person" Stance Thinking

In order to change your "unique person" stance thinking, you will need to

- learn to set realistic standards for yourself and others

- accept that you will make mistakes—it's inevitable for all human beings—and realize that you can learn from your failures

- understand that nothing of value ever comes easily

- begin to solve problems by finding out the facts first

- resist believing that you are different from others

- develop humility, an understanding of what you are and what you are not

That last one, develop humility, is one of the most difficult for criminal thinkers to understand because they confuse humility with humiliation. Yes, humility means not being arrogant or boastful, but it does *not* mean being weak or submissive. Humility is a position of strength, because it is grounded in honest self-knowledge and can therefore be trusted. When you claim to be a simple, decent person and then follow that up with responsible behavior, that's humility. No one can doubt you or bring you down because you are living your word, and you know the truth about yourself. And no one can take that away.

Humiliation, on the other hand, is the logical result of trying to live in a stance, or pose. Claiming to be a smart criminal and ending up behind bars is humiliation. When you set yourself apart from others in a "unique person" stance, you are inviting humiliation.

Humility means not being arrogant or boastful.

Uniqueness in Perspective:
"I'm Just an Ordinary Person"

➤ 1. This week when you are thinking about asking for something special because of your "uniqueness," stop and write down

What was the situation?

_____

_____

What did you do to stop yourself?

_____

_____

➤ 2. This week when you are thinking you are better than "ordinary" people, stop yourself and write down

What was the situation?

_____

_____

What did you do to stop yourself?

_____

_____

Fear of Exposure

Fear is not necessarily a bad thing. Rational, healthy fears guide us every day. A rational fear of dying may keep you from jumping from a high place. A fear of crashing may lead you to drive sanely. A fear of losing everything you have may prevent you from taking a risky criminal venture or from gambling all that you own.

As a criminal thinker, you probably like to pose as fearless. In fact, your reckless behavior may give others that impression. You may even believe that you *are* invincible. The truth is, however, that you are consumed with fears: fear that you are a nobody, fear that others will find you out, fear of all your thoughts and actions being brought out into the open and judged. This is called **fear of exposure,** and much of your thinking is driven by it. One of your biggest fears is the fear of fear!

Like other criminal thinkers, you also expect injury or early death. There is a common belief among criminal thinkers that they will have a short life and painful death. You use this as an excuse to commit crimes.

You also are likely to fear any kind of putdown. You think that to tolerate a criticism would be to let someone else control you. You're so jumpy; you often view *positive* feedback as a putdown.

This is all part of the criminal thinking pattern called fear of exposure. There are four main aspects of fear of exposure:

- fear of vulnerability
- lack of trust
- criminal pride
- zero state

Fear of Vulnerability

As a criminal thinker, you fear appearing weak and inadequate to anyone, even nonthreatening people such as young children. One reason is your fear of death or injury, a fear that you think about all the time.

You're also afraid that if you let anyone see the real you, you will be humiliated. Your fear of humiliation is powerful. It pushes you to commit a number of antisocial and self-defeating behaviors, such as

- getting into a lot of fights
- pushing away the people who genuinely care for you

There is a high price to pay for your fear of vulnerability. You have given up closeness with another person, *any* person. This is because you cannot be close to someone without being vulnerable to him or her. And that requires trust.

Lack of Trust

A major aspect of the criminal thinking pattern fear of exposure is a lack of trust. One reason for this is that when you are constantly trying to get away with criminal activity, you are *always* vulnerable to being exposed or caught. You've always got something to hide.

Your criminal behavior is your weak spot.

All someone has to do is call the cops and you're busted. Since you fear being exposed or caught and your criminal behavior makes you vulnerable, you're suspicious of everyone. You think just about everyone else is a con man, just like you. You don't even trust your criminal partners—and they don't trust you. Criminal thinkers are always holding back some information from their criminal associates. They are always trying to protect themselves by getting something on each other—*just in case.*

Criminal Pride

Criminal pride shows itself in fighting, bragging, refusing to admit you don't know something, and believing that your type of crime is better than the other guy's type of crime.

It is really important to you that you get what you think is "respect" from others. You are always thinking about who respects you and who doesn't. But think about it: If you had true *self*-respect, you wouldn't need the "respect" of others so badly.

The fact is, you don't have much true self-respect. Underneath it all, you're scared that without all your stances and postures, you are nothing.

Zero State

If you dare to think you are not unique or special, what little self-respect you have drops to zero. This is called the zero state. The zero state consists of these beliefs:

- You are nothing.

- Everyone else also believes you are worthless.

- Your "worthlessness" will last forever and can never be changed.

Criminal zero-state thinkers are also angry and want to victimize others. Being in the zero state is uncomfortable. You want to do something "powerful" to get yourself out of the zero state, like hurting other people.

In the zero state, your values are backward. You think normal, appropriate, and healthy behaviors are signs of weakness. This includes thinking and behavior such as

- the willingness to compromise with loved ones

- the ability to admit mistakes and take responsibility

- the willingness to learn from mistakes and move on

- the patience to set goals and work toward them, even at the risk of failure

If you were a hero, you wouldn't be where you are now: addicted to alcohol or other drugs and incarcerated.

Correcting Fear of Exposure

In order to change your fear of exposure, you will need to do the following:

- become more self-aware

- develop realistic expectations for yourself and others

- let go of false pride and accept a basic humility that helps you know who you really are—neither a "hero" nor a "zero"

- replace your desire for domination with a desire for cooperation and partnership—especially in your closest personal relationships

- learn to assess the integrity of others accurately

- come to trust honest and well-meaning people who can help you in life

- be guided by healthy and accurate fears rather than fear of the zero state or no fear

You have to work toward these goals steadily; try to learn a little something and practice it every day. Recovering alcoholics deal with the same things.

You may not like the idea of giving up your big-shot, hero status. But the truth is, it was a lie all along. If you were a hero, you wouldn't be where you are now: addicted to alcohol or other drugs and incarcerated. That may seem like the bad news, but it really isn't. When you give up the idea that you're some kind of superhero, you also get to give up feeling that you're worthless, empty, nothing. Because that's not true about you either. And *that's* the good news.

Now you just have to find what that "something" is. When you do, you will discover who you really are.

Learning to Bend

Because of their fear of exposure, criminal thinkers tend to be rigid in their thinking. The fact is, however, that a *real* man can bend and be flexible. Here are some examples of rigid fear-of-exposure thinking:

- "It's against my principles to give in."

- "What right did he have to question my motives?"

- "I'm not going to let him think I'm weak. No one puts me down."

➤ On which issues do you find it difficult to give in?

1. _____

2. _____

3. _____

Recall a time when you were overly sensitive to a challenge most people would consider normal.

EXAMPLE:

> *In group someone tells you, "I don't see you being willing to own up to your crime yet."*

➤ Describe the incident.

_____

_____

_____

➤ What was your first reaction?

_____

_____

➤ What could you tell yourself—how could you challenge your thoughts—so you could respond more flexibly?

_____

_____

➤ How could you have responded differently by being more flexible?

_____

_____

➤ List three things you can be truly proud of having done (that your conscience tells you are good and right).

1. _____

_____

2. _____

_____

3. _____

_____

EXERCISE 24 EXERCISE

Interrupting the Zero State

As you've learned, living in the zero state is unbearable and you will do almost anything to get out of it. Not realizing that the zero state is temporary, you fool yourself into thinking that anything—even being incarcerated—would be better. That's one way you justify your criminal behavior to yourself. Here are some examples of this kind of thinking:

- "I'd rather be serving time than be straight like you."

- "I can't stand it anymore. I'm going to find some excitement."

- "There's no hope for me. I've been following the program and I have more problems than ever."

To interrupt zero-state thinking, you need to try to see the big picture of your life. One way is to identify the good things you have done or tried to do.

➤ List something about you that is especially worthwhile— something you've done or a quality you have that, if used responsibly, could bring you success and help others.

_____

_____

_____

_____

At first, it is difficult to get out of the zero state by yourself. That is why one of the best ways to interrupt the zero state responsibly is to call someone you trust and talk it through.

Lack-of-Time Perspective

Another feature of your thinking is a **lack-of-time perspective.** There are three parts to this criminal thinking pattern:

1. You do not learn from past experiences and do not think about the future. You see behaviors as isolated events. You do not clearly grasp the idea of *cause and effect,* which means that when you do A (cause), then B (effect) happens. Sometimes you even reverse the idea (thinking the result was really the cause). Therefore, you are likely to think, "This time will be different," and indulge the same thoughts and repeat the same behaviors that have failed you before.

2. You believe in the ***instant gratification*** of desires. Your philosophy is "I want it, and I want it *now*." You expect others to act on your demands immediately, and you tend be ***impulsive*** in most areas of your life.

3. You expect to be a big success with only minimal effort and preparation, and you fantasize constantly about making the "big score." You do not set achievable goals or make realistic plans. You often base your decisions on whims and assumptions that are rarely supported by facts. You make choices based on what you *want* to be true rather than what is true.

Instant Gratification

Instant gratification means satisfying a desire or need immediately, without planning or effort.

Impulsive

Impulsive means acting on the spur of the moment, without much thought or consideration. Most crimes are committed impulsively.

As a result of these three problems, your thinking gets you into serious trouble on a regular basis. You don't think things through. You don't consider the situation from several angles to see the possible consequences. Therefore, you lack the sound decision-making process you need for responsible living. Your decision-making is compromised in three ways:

1. You act impulsively, on the spur of the moment, to satisfy your need for instant gratification.

2. You avoid seeking facts, because it shows you don't know the answer and you may have to ask others for help.

3. You have tunnel vision. You focus only on what is in front of you and the easiest way to get it rather than seeing the whole range of options available.

The decisions you make tend to be the ones that inflate your image the most or else seem to be the easiest way. Sometimes, you make decisions by default. This happens when you avoid making a decision by refusing to recognize that a problem exists. When the consequences of failing to make a responsible decision hit you, as they always do, you claim to be a victim of random events you did not choose. You do not understand that refusing to choose is often a choice in itself.

Adding Up the Time

➤ Refer back to exercise 2 on page 12, Your Criminal History. Add up all of the time you've spent incarcerated and write it here. (Include juvenile detention, jail time done even when you weren't prosecuted, detox, and every other place where you were detained by the justice system.)

_____ years   _____ months

Correcting the Lack-of-Time Perspective in Your Thinking
As exercise 25 shows, your desire for instant gratification, your inability to understand cause and effect, and your lack of planning have had a cost. They have cost you, your family, your victims and their families, and the rest of society. And they have cost *a lot*—in time, money, and meaningless suffering. To correct this disastrous thinking pattern, you need to do the following:

- change from thinking in terms of instant gratification to thinking in terms of goals

- identify your patterns of thinking and behavior that have had severe negative results in your life

- learn to base your current and future decisions on a thorough examination of the facts

- understand and accept that responsible payoffs are not immediate and that time, effort, and patience are needed to plan for and achieve worthwhile goals

Responsible Choices

➤ Think about one of the crimes that you have been incarcerated for and list, as clearly as possible, three irresponsible choices you made that led to that crime. List them in the order that they occurred. In the second column, write down responsible alternative choices you *could* have made each time.

Crime: _____

Irresponsible choices you made	Responsible choices you could have made
1. _____	_____
_____	_____
_____	_____
2. _____	_____
_____	_____
_____	_____
3. _____	_____
_____	_____
_____	_____

Selective Effort

The sixth criminal thinking pattern you use is **selective effort.** People put forth *effort* not because it's necessarily fun, or provides a rush, or seems like the thing to do in the moment. Effort is not impulsive. It means putting a plan into motion. Work is effort. Study is effort. Training and exercise are effort. Doing what is required of you in this treatment program is effort.

As a criminal thinker, you use *selective* effort. In fact, you may do almost anything you can to avoid responsible effort. You may put out a great deal of energy, especially in your criminal pursuits. But when it comes to effort, you tend to avoid it at all costs. Usually you do this by saying, "I can't." What you really mean is, "I won't."

This is not to suggest that you don't start a lot of new projects. You've most likely had a lot of energy and were always busy cooking up one kind of a scheme or another. Sometimes you may even become totally preoccupied with one of your activities, to the point where you let go of nearly everything else, including eating and sleeping. But eventually you become bored with it, particularly if problems or setbacks result. Then it begins to seem more like effort, and that's when you quit.

You therefore tend to be selective about your efforts, like most criminal thinkers.

You either avoid something when you can't make a quick gain, or you bail out as soon as effort becomes necessary.

When it comes to effort, you lose your energy really fast, despite your history of having a lot of energy for impulsive criminal activity.

Selective effort can be summed up in these mental traits:

- refuses to move through obstacles or stressful circumstances

- becomes bored with anything requiring work (effort) over time

- feels ***entitled*** to material things without having to earn them

Correcting Selective Effort

Correcting selective-effort thinking means giving up the "I can't (I won't)" attitude. No meaningful change is possible as long as you hold on to it. If you think about it, the "I can't (I won't)" attitude you made part of your personal thought map leaves you with only three options:

1. You can continue with your criminal behavior and spend your life behind bars or on the run.

2. You can commit suicide (and the suicide rate is very high among prisoners compared with the general population).

3. Or you can let go of the "I can't (I won't)" attitude and begin making the changes that will lead to recovery and a responsible life.

That's it. Three options.
We suggest option number three.

If you choose recovery and responsibility, you have changed "I can't (I won't)" to "I *must*." That may seem like a small thing, but it's not. Once you start saying, "I *must*," you have taken a huge step toward a different kind of life.

The second part of changing your selective-effort thinking is learning how to set goals and plan the steps to reach them. As a criminal thinker, you have a difficult time with this. Your track record for taking more than a few steps toward any meaningful goal is poor. This does not mean you

Practice taking one step today toward something better.

can't learn how to succeed at setting goals and following through now. Using past failure to not try is just an excuse. You can learn to set a responsible goal and maintain responsible behavior as you move toward it simply by practicing taking one step today toward something better. You have heard that sobriety comes "one day at a time." The same is true of responsible living.

You Can—and You Must

➤ You must adopt an attitude of *doing:* taking the first step toward something better, making an effort to try things differently, even if there doesn't seem to be an immediate payoff. Even if it doesn't look like fun. Even if there are obstacles. To do this, it's helpful to really understand what you can and can't do.

Some things you *can't* do	Some things you *can* do
You can't change anybody but yourself.	You *can* change yourself.
You can't change the past.	You *can* change the future.
You can't always get your own way.	You *can* change what you think and do when you don't get your own way.
You can't always pick and choose the problems you have to face in your life.	You *can* decide how to handle these problems.

Here are some examples of "I can't (I won't)" selective-effort thinking:

- "Being a parent is boring—and raising the kids ain't my job anyway."

- "My wife asks too much of me. I care about her, but not enough to put up with her nagging."

- "If I can't be the boss, I don't want the job."

➤ What things do you usually say "I can't" to? Listen to yourself this week and write them down.

1. _____

2. _____

3. _____

➤ One time this week, when you find yourself starting to say (or thinking about saying), "I can't," instead say, "I can" and go ahead and do it. Write down what happened.

_____

_____

_____

_____

_____

Setting Goals

➤ List two goals you would like to achieve in the future. *Keep them realistic and attainable.* (Playing in the NBA does not qualify. Becoming a doctor does not qualify. Getting a high school diploma or completing a job training course would qualify.)

Goal #1

_____

Goal #2

_____

➤ List the steps you could take to reach each of these goals. List them in the order you think they should be done.

Steps to reach goal #1

1. _____

2. _____

3. _____

4. _____

5. _____

➤ Steps to reach goal #2

1. _____

2. _____

3. _____

4. _____

5. _____

➤ List some barriers or obstacles, things that get in your way, that you may have to overcome to reach each goal.

Barriers or obstacles to achieving goal #1

1. _____

2. _____

3. _____

Barriers or obstacles to achieving goal #2

1. _____

2. _____

3. _____

Use of Power to Control

As a criminal thinker, you often think in ways that involve the **use of power to control** others and get your own way. This power is not legitimate power, such as the power to create, to right a wrong, or to effect change for the better. It is not power earned through hard work, study, and the gaining of experience and knowledge. It is also not power that comes from discipline, self-control, and self-knowledge. Your criminal thinking type of power is none of these things. It is power used to manipulate, intimidate, humiliate, and dominate others for your own excitement and to get what you want.

The thinking that drives you to use power to control is motivated by selfishness. You do it because controlling others makes *you* feel good. It is a crude strategy to avoid the zero state (feeling like you are nothing) that we discussed earlier. Using power to control is also the direction your thoughts take when victim-stance thinking doesn't work for you. If you can't manipulate others by gaining their sympathy, you try to do it through fear and intimidation.

Examples of this kind of thinking include the following:

- "Do unto others before they do unto you."
- "Man, you don't know who you're messin' with."
- "I'm not letting no girlfriend tell me what to do."
- "The best defense is a good offense."

Using power to control can involve in-your-face verbal or physical threats of force (actual threats or just suggestions of "bad things" that could happen). It can also be quiet, behind-the-scenes manipulation of others or slick con-man talk. No matter how it is used, chances are the thinking that leads you to use power to control has been with you a long time and dominates much of your life.

Fantasies of conquest and being respected or even "worshiped" are very common with you in areas of sex, work, and social life. Sometimes you actually believe you are worshiped. These are powerful delusions, but they *are* delusions. It is impossible to control all the situations and people you come in contact with.

Even when you do succeed in getting people to comply, they only do it out of fear.

Respect is something you crave and demand from others, but it is also something you don't really understand.

Correcting Your Use of Power to Control

Have you ever wondered why you're so angry all the time? Have you noticed that other criminals—the people you hang out with, do crime with, or serve time with—are also very angry people? There are many reasons for your anger, but one of the main ones is the thinking pattern called *use of power to control.*

Trying to control everyone and everything all the time takes a lot of energy. A *whole* lot of energy. It's really hard work. Not only that, it's impossible! You can't control anyone or anything except your own thinking and behavior, so it's doomed to fail. Think about it for a moment. Here you have a task (using power to control others) that you have devoted much of your life to and which is draining and frustrating and guaranteed to fail. No wonder you're angry all the time!

This anger may be expressed outright or may be just boiling beneath the surface, flashing out at unpredictable times. Much of your anger (and one of the reasons you try to use power to control) is your fear of being dissed, put down, humiliated. Your reaction to a perceived putdown is anger to reestablish control. But since you're always trying

Have you ever wondered why you're so angry all the time?

to control and never really succeeding for any length of time, you're almost always feeling put down. That's why when things happen to you that don't fit with your immediate desires, you see it as some form of disrespect. This leads to a near-constant state of anger and almost always trying to gain the upper hand through intimidation or undermining of others.

It's a vicious circle: attempts to control lead to perceived disrespect, which leads to anger, which puts you in the zero state, which leads to more attempts to control to get out of the zero state.

Figure 9
THE VICIOUS CIRCLE

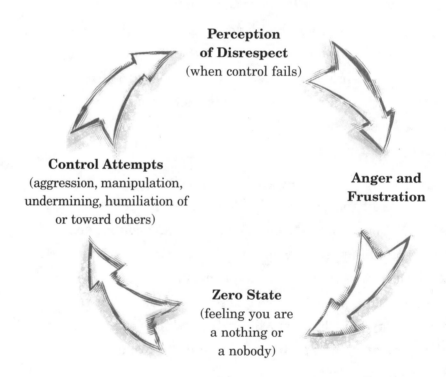

**Perception
of Disrespect**
(when control fails)

**Anger and
Frustration**

Zero State
(feeling you are
a nothing or
a nobody)

Control Attempts
(aggression, manipulation,
undermining, humiliation of
or toward others)

The only way out of this vicious circle is to learn to manage your anger and step away from the need to control. The truth is, you can control very little of your environment. You do not have the right or the ability to control others. Again, to dominate others is not to lead them; to frighten others is not to have their respect.

You can't control anyone or anything except your own thinking and behavior.

Using Power to Control

➤ Identify three ways that you use power to control others.

1. _____

   _____

2. _____

   _____

3. _____

   _____

➤ Check with your peers in the group. Ask them to identify three ways to control people that they have seen you use and that are different from the three you listed above.

1. _____

   _____

2. _____

   _____

3. _____

   _____

Real Feelings of Anger

Anger is normal. Everybody feels anger from time to time. As a criminal thinker, however, you feel something that is often not even real anger. Rather, it is something you show to others as a threat to try to control them. When you do experience real anger, however, you can quickly lose control of it and become very destructive.

➤ List three recent situations when you were angry. If you think it was a real feeling of anger, place an **X** under "real." If you showed anger just to intimidate someone, place an **X** under "show."

Situation	Real	Show
1. _____	_____	_____
_____		
_____		
2. _____	_____	_____
_____		
_____		
3. _____	_____	_____
_____		
_____		

Seek Excitement First

One of the criminal thinking patterns that gets you into trouble the quickest is **seek excitement first.** The thoughts that urge you to seek excitement first keep you uninterested in a lot of responsible behavior. Here are some of the features of this type of thinking:

- You can't tolerate boredom.

- You can't stand being alone for more than short periods of time.

- You can't stay at a task (or a job) for long periods of time.

- You avoid obligations because they're too dull— they get in the way of your excitement.

- You seek excitement (especially through crime, drugs, and sex) on the spur of the moment. You live for today.

- Your thoughts of excitement are so powerful, they tend to push away any thoughts about consequences or what your conscience tells you.

- You think you're "nobody's sucker" when it comes to *responsible* living, but you're an easy mark to the *irresponsible* suggestions of others.

It's easy to see why you have probably found it difficult to hold on to a job for very long. One of the main reasons you struggle to hold a job is your desire to seek excitement first.

The problem is, *no* job is exciting enough for you. You move from one job to another chasing something that probably doesn't exist. And that leads you right to criminal behavior.

The thoughts that urge you to seek excitement first keep you uninterested in a lot of responsible behavior.

Correcting "Seek Excitement First" Thinking

Responsible action is difficult for you. You're simply not used to it. Saying no to excitement will take some work. One way to change your "seek excitement first" thinking is to try to think "as if"—that is, practice thinking about doing the responsible thing even when it feels strange or uncomfortable or boring. Then follow through with action.

If you think and act as if you were responsible, eventually it will become a habit. In the end, you will *be* responsible—and receive the rewards of responsible living. These rewards are much greater than you think they are right now.

When is the right moment to practice thinking "as if"? It's when you begin to feel the surge of excitement you get from thinking about risky, irresponsible behavior. This feeling is called criminal excitement.

 EXERCISE 31 EXERCISE

Criminal Excitement

Crime can be addictive. Just as you can be addicted to alcohol or other drugs, you also can be addicted to criminal excitement. Here are some examples:

- You have $30 for groceries, enough to get what you need, but you decide to shoplift the food just for kicks.
- You see a car idling in a parking lot, and you jump in and go for a joy ride.

Some of the things you do for criminal excitement aren't crimes, but they reinforce the "seek excitement first" thinking pattern. Here are some examples:

- trash talking on the basketball court—really trying to push the other guy to the edge
- telling old criminal "war stories" to relive the rush of excitement

➤ List two examples of criminal excitement, even if you
didn't actually end up committing a crime at the time.
These are things you did mainly to get a rush.

1. _____

_____

2. _____

_____

➤ What thoughts went through your head at the time of these
experiences? List one thought for each example you gave.

1. _____

_____

2. _____

_____

➤ What obligations or responsibilities did you blow off to
follow that excitement?

1. _____

_____

2. _____

_____

Consequences of
"Seek Excitement First" Thinking

Because you tend to do only what brings immediate gratification and excitement, you have lost out on experiences
that have deeper meaning. You have missed chances to
grow, learn, and become a better person. You may have
turned your back on career possibilities, being with family,
or other opportunities.

➤ What goals or responsible experiences have you given up
or lost because they weren't exciting?

1. _____

2. _____

3. _____

➤ Describe what your life might look like if you had followed
through on some of those goals and experiences.

_____

_____

_____

_____

Failure to Take Responsible Action

There are many ways you fail to take responsible action. Here are some examples:

- You make an excuse to quit a job because it's "too much of a hassle."

- You think, "There's no guarantee I'll get a good job anyway, so I'm quitting school."

- You decide, "I tried to be responsible and it didn't work out the way I wanted, so I won't make the mistake of trying again."

➤ List three times you failed to take responsible action this past week.

1. _____

2. _____

3. _____

➤ What were you thinking when you blew off the responsible action that you were called to do or had an opportunity to do?

_____

_____

_____

_____

Ownership Stance

Ownership-stance thinking gives you a distorted idea about what are your rights and your property and what are the rights and property of others. It's one of the big reasons you are locked up right now. This thinking allows you to violate others or their property. When you use ownership-stance thinking, you do not see the difference between things that belong to you and those that belong to others—maybe because you think *everything* belongs to you. It also leads you to see others as your property to control and do with as you please. Your ownership stance prevents you from realizing that other people are independent human beings who have their own dreams, goals, desires, and purpose. Ownership-stance thinking can therefore be summed up as follows:

- one-way property boundaries ("What's mine is mine, and what's yours is mine.")

- the idea that people are property ("She's mine, so she has to do as I say.")

Sexual Ownership Stance

One of the ways you think about people as your property is with your sexuality. You think the purpose of others is to provide for your life needs, including your sexual needs. Most likely, you fantasize often about controlling others sexually. To get sex, you will manipulate, con, intimidate, lie, use force, or you will buy sex with drugs or money. You do this because of your ownership-stance thinking: You think the people you are attracted to owe you sex, simply because you want it. Because you think they owe it to you, you think it's okay to get it any way you can.

Your ownership stance prevents you from realizing that other people are independent human beings.

Correcting Ownership-Stance Thinking

One of the first things you need to do to correct your ownership stance is to start thinking differently about your relationships with others. You will need to learn to see other people as equal human beings. They are separate from you and have their own rights and property. What they do is for them to decide, not you. What they own is theirs, not yours.

You do have a connection with the people who are in your life. A healthy life in recovery requires that you learn to understand that connection and keep it in balance.

The truth is, we are all **interdependent** on one another. That means you need others and others need you. Healthy interdependence is a mix of dependent and independent thoughts and acts.

Finally, to change your ownership-stance thinking, you need to learn that property rights go two ways, not just one. You think that once you take something, it's yours. It's not. Just because you took it from someone doesn't mean it now belongs to you. In the same sense, you do not own things you have tricked someone into giving you through lies, threats, or empty promises.

The only things you own in life are your own thoughts and character and the material things you have earned through responsible effort.

Interdependence

Interdependence in human relationships means sharing needs with others in a mutually agreed upon exchange. In its most basic form, it's like the old saying "You scratch my back and I'll scratch yours." But it really means much more than that. In a deeper sense, interdependence means living in a healthy way in which you give to and receive from your spouse or partner, family, community, society, and nature so that *most* life needs for you and for others around you can be met *most* of the time.

Character vs. Reputation

Character is about your moral strength. It comes from finding the best qualities inside yourself, believing in them, and showing them every day in your behavior. Character is something you learn about yourself and then act on no matter what others may think.

Reputation is only about the image you try to get *others* to believe in. Most of the time, your reputation is just a con. It's your attempt to make others—and yourself—believe you are something that you're not.

> *"Be more concerned about your character than your reputation, because your character is what you really are, while your reputation is merely what others think you are."*
>
> —John Wooden, legendary UCLA basketball coach

EXERCISE **34** EXERCISE

Two-Way Property Boundaries

As an example of how he was really a decent guy ("good person" stance), an inmate told a story about how, when his girlfriend brought home the money from her welfare check, he let her keep $50 of it to go buy herself something nice at Wal-Mart.

➤ How is this also an example of ownership-stance criminal thinking?

_____

_____

_____

➤ List three pieces of property in your cell that you think belong to you.

1. _____

2. _____

3. _____

➤ How did you get these things?

_____

_____

➤ What would you think if someone stole these things or conned you out of them?

_____

_____

If you have not already done so, you are now ready to start identifying the criminal thinking patterns you use and adding them to your Thinking Reports. You can also begin identifying different, healthier alternative thoughts. Both your criminal thinking patterns and alternative thoughts can be added to your worksheet on page 49 of part 2.

Addictive Thinking Patterns

Addictive thinking patterns are very similar to criminal thinking patterns. In most cases, the only differences are in degree or in the particular direction the thinking takes. Remember the definition of criminal thinking patterns? *Criminal thinking patterns* are ways of thinking that say it is okay to violate others or the property of others.

The definition of addictive thinking patterns is similar: *Addictive thinking patterns* are ways of thinking that say it is okay to use as much drugs and alcohol as you want, as often as you want, and to do whatever you need to do to get them.

*Addiction is a **thinking** problem before it becomes a **drinking** problem.*

Thoughts that suggest, justify, or promote getting drunk and high no matter what the consequences to you or to others will most likely fit into one or more of the addictive thinking patterns categories.

Here are the addictive thinking patterns we've identified:

- self-pity stance
- "good person" stance
- "unique person" stance
- fear of exposure
- lack-of-time perspective
- selective effort
- use of deceit to control
- seek pleasure first
- ownership stance

As an addict, you are pleasure-centered and self-centered.

Denial

The main feature of addictive thinking is ***denial.*** Denial for the addict and alcoholic refers to the ability to contradict obvious facts, to turn the truth inside out, to look directly at *down* and to believe, with all your heart and mind, that it is really *up.*

One of the interesting features of denial is that you can often see in others what you can't see in yourself. You can't see how your alcohol or other drug use has gotten you in so much trouble that you've lost just about everything. Now you're incarcerated, probably not for the first time.

You haven't been able to see the truth about your own alcohol or other drug use because of your denial. To see that truth would mean you'd have to try recovery. It would mean you'd have to stop using. And that is what your addictive thinking calls you to deny—anything that would suggest you need to stop using.

Denial

Denial is used by addicts and alcoholics to keep themselves unaware of the harmful consequences of their use. Though addicts and alcoholics often lie to get what they want, denial is not about lying to others. Denial is a trick the addict's mind plays on itself to excuse the use of alcohol or other drugs no matter what harm it does.

Denial is not a river in Egypt.

Self-Obsession

As an addict, you are pleasure-centered and self-centered. That means your thoughts focus on whether or not you feel good. If you don't feel good, you become preoccupied with what you can do to make yourself feel good again as soon as possible. You had a powerful pleasure experience with drugs or alcohol (or with sex or gambling or eating or anything else people get addicted to) when you first used, and your mind became obsessed with repeating that experience. When you feel bad, all you can think about is how to get drugs (alcohol, sex, and so on) so you will feel like you felt that first time you experienced them.

Because you are obsessed with feeling good, you tend to think only about your own wants and needs. Only after your wants and needs are met (for the moment, at least) are you able to consider the wants and needs of others.

Irrational Thinking

Because your thinking is driven by the obsession to feel good, it becomes *irrational*. Irrational thoughts lead to out-of-whack emotions and irrational behavior.

As an addict, you often use irrational thinking because you are not looking to find the truth. You are only looking to justify and excuse your single-minded search for the high. That is why your logic usually goes around in circles, even when it may seem to make sense on the surface.

Self-Pity Stance

As an addict, you have your own version of the victim-stance criminal thinking pattern. It's called the **self-pity stance.** You think the world is out to get you, that you're just a victim of bad luck. You have a hard time taking responsibility for what happens to you. You see yourself as the victim. In fact, if you're really pushed, you'd likely accept any explanation for how miserable and screwed up your life can be—as long as that explanation doesn't point a finger at your drug or alcohol use.

That *is* insane thinking. But it's not the result of mental illness—it's the result of your addiction to alcohol or other drugs.

Poor me. Poor me. Poor me.

Pour me . . . a drink.

Irrational Thinking

Irrational thinking is thinking that is inconsistent with the facts. It contradicts itself and is confused, disorderly, and distorted. Irrational thinking does not use reason to find the truth; it makes arguments to try to prove a lie.

Identifying Self-Pity Thinking

Self-pity thinking is one important way you justify your use of alcohol or other drugs. The following thoughts are examples of the self-pity stance:

- "I grew up in a tough neighborhood. I had to fight for survival. Having a hit or two now and then is the least I deserve for all I went through."

- "My dad was a drunk and my mom shot heroin. It's not my fault I use."

- "When I was in school, I always got punished for stuff I didn't do. Life's always been unfair to me."

➤ List three self-pitying thoughts you had last week.

1. _____

2. _____

3. _____

➤ Explain how your self-pity stance has set you up to use in the past.

_____

_____

_____

Despite all the things you've messed up, you still think you're a decent person.

"Good Person" Stance

Despite all the things you've messed up and all the times you've let yourself and other people down, you still think you're a decent person. As an addictive thinker, you use four main strategies to create and maintain the illusion that you are essentially a good person, no matter what. They are the same strategies you use as a criminal thinker, only you also use them to justify your chemical use. These strategies are

- sentimentality
- selective memory
- excuses and rationalizations
- false comparisons and self-serving definitions

You use these strategies to avoid thinking about yourself realistically. If you saw yourself clearly and realistically, it would be obvious even to you how drugs or alcohol have messed up your life and led you to hurt yourself and others. The purpose of "good person" stance thinking, like all other addictive thinking patterns, is to justify your continued use.

As an addictive thinker using the "good person" stance, you focus on the good things you've done and ignore the harm. You get *sentimental* about your mother but forget the times you lied to her or stole from her. Or you talk about how much your kids mean to you, even though you can't remember their birthdays. Or you try to make yourself look good by continually pointing out that someone else is worse than you. You say, "At least I'm not a crack head," or "I'm no gutter drunk like that guy." You believe in an addictive hierarchy just like you believe in a criminal hierarchy. The idea that some drugs are somehow "better" than other drugs, however, is delusional. They all do the same thing to your brain in the end—they hijack it. And they'll all kill you, sooner or later.

Sentimentality

Sentimentality is viewing your motives and intentions as always "good" on some level.

Your Hierarchy of Drug Use

➤ List your hierarchy of drugs in order, from the "best" to the worst/most degrading. (Remember, alcohol *is* a drug.)

1. _____

2. _____

3. _____

4. _____

5. _____

➤ What makes drugs 1 and 2 better drugs to use? What makes drugs 4 and 5 worse drugs to use?

_____

_____

_____

➤ How do you use your hierarchy of drugs to justify your own chemical use?

_____

_____

_____

_____

"Unique Person" Stance

As an addictive thinker, you like to see yourself as different and special. You also tend to romanticize yourself. You may see yourself as a mysterious, adventurous, or tragic figure, like a pirate or an old-west cowboy or a gangster or some other super-bad, super-tough character.

You also think you are always right and have great difficulty admitting your mistakes. You are self-righteous. That means you will do whatever it takes to prove you are right—shouting down others, arguing over every little thing, bullying others into agreement or silence.

You use the **"unique person" stance** to feed your addiction. Perhaps you think your drug or alcohol use makes you especially cool—the hard drinker/smoker/snorter who can use more than anyone else and still be standing at the end of the night.

Your addiction is really the least unique thing about you. The truth is, you have a very common disease that has clear symptoms, familiar thought and behavior patterns, and predictable results. The story of your addiction is more or less the same as every other addict's story.

Here are examples of addictive thinking using the "unique person" stance:

- "I can drink anybody under the table."
- "Crack takes me places you can't even dream of."
- "I've smuggled more junk without getting caught than you'll ever see in your lifetime."
- "Don't tell me about what drugs do. I've forgotten more about chemicals than you'll ever know."

As an addictive thinker, you like to see yourself as different and special.

Your So-Called Unique Addiction

➤ List two things you have told yourself that were different about your alcohol or other drug use than anybody else's.

1. _____

   _____

2. _____

   _____

■

Fear of Exposure

Just as your criminal thinking patterns are filled with many fears, so are your addictive thinking patterns. Here are four features of addictive **fear of exposure:**

- fear of self-knowledge
- excessive or inappropriate trust
- addict pride
- zero state

The first three represent a fear of change. You fear you'll be exposed as an addict or alcoholic and will have to stop using. So you hide your use or you flaunt it. You hide it so others won't know about your use and challenge it, or you flaunt it as a power move to make it seem like nothing can hurt you. Either way, you are afraid to take a good, hard look at your chemical use because you are afraid of changing your life in ways that might mean changing your use.

The zero state represents a fear that you cannot change, that you will get trapped in an intolerable condition of emptiness. In the zero state, you are frantic to change—though the *only* thing you really want to change is how bad you feel.

Fear of Self-Knowledge

You are afraid that if you really found out who you are, deep down, you might see that you are nothing. This is fear of the zero state that we discussed in criminal thinking patterns. You avoid self-knowledge to avoid looking at this fear—the fear that you might be worthless.

Excessive or Inappropriate Trust

As an addict, you base trust on who might help you get high and who won't. You tend to trust untrustworthy people who promise to help you get high. You tend to distrust trustworthy people who discourage or try to block your chemical use. Your trust is not based on facts or logic or even your own good sense of who is honest and who isn't.

Addict Pride

Most addicts have a sense of pride about their drug of choice. They think it is somehow better than other drugs. So a crack smoker might think heroin addicts are degraded for injecting their drug, while heroin addicts might say crack users are sick for how they can desperately chase the high for days on end in the worst conditions. Alcoholics may think their drug is better because it's legal, while ecstasy users think theirs is the coolest drug.

Zero State

As an addict, you also go into the zero state from time to time—the belief that you are worthless, nobody, empty inside. While your criminal thinking tends to use power over others as a way to escape the zero state, your addictive thinking tends to use deceit to control others or increased chemical use to find relief. In both cases, however, you will use both deceit and power to escape zero state, and you'll often use them together. As an addict *and* a criminal, you will use any of those strategies—whatever seems to work at the time.

As an addict, you tend to look on the dark side of things. You expect the worst and often see the worst in situations and others. Just as you use your expectation of an early death to justify your criminal behavior, you use the same dark thinking as an excuse to get high. You think, "If I'm doomed anyway, why not?"

Despite your thoughts of impending doom, when it comes to your chemical use, you also have an irrational belief that alcohol and other drugs will not have a harmful effect on your body and brain. You assume they won't have the same destructive results on your body that they have on everyone else's. You assume that just because the chemicals are medically proven to be addictive to human beings and millions of users did become addicted, you are somehow the exception. It won't (or didn't) happen to you.

So either you *deny* the harm of chemical use or you accept it because you don't care, since you're doomed anyway.

You also lack healthy fears that would keep you from harm, especially in regard to your chemical use. That is why you are willing to put some pill or powder you bought from a dealer you may not even know into your body. Because getting high is more important to you than your own physical safety, you are willing to believe exactly what the dealer tells you. You trust this even when you know the dealer to be a highly untrustworthy person!

Risk Taking

➤ Give three examples of serious risks you have taken to get high.

1. _____

2. _____

3. _____

➤ Is there anything else in your life (besides chemicals) that is so attractive it would lead you to take such risks? If so, what is it?

_____

_____

Lack-of-Time Perspective

Because getting high (feeling intense pleasure) is the most important thing in your life, you tend to live only in the present when you are high and only in the near future ("How can I get more soon?") when you are not high. This **lack-of-time perspective** is one feature of your thinking that denies the health damage and social consequences of using by blocking out thoughts of the long-term future.

Your lack-of-time perspective also shows up in how you get cause and effect mixed up. *Cause and effect* means that when you do A (cause), then B (effect) happens. For example, if you jump in a lake (cause), you will get wet (effect).

It seems pretty simple. But what about the following causes and effects?

- If you steal your girlfriend's money to buy drugs (cause), she will get angry and upset and nag you about your irresponsibility (effect).

- If you get drunk all the time (cause), you will lose your job (effect).

In the addict's deluded (reversed) version of cause and effect, the thinking goes like this:

- Because my girlfriend nags and gets angry all the time (cause), I get high (effect).

- Because they fire me from every job (cause), I drink (effect).

By reversing cause and effect in the moment, you fail to look at what happened in the past—that your chemical use created serious problems. You also can't see what will happen in the future—that more serious problems will be caused by continued use of alcohol and other drugs if you don't stop now. Your chemical use is not the *result* of your problems; it is the primary *cause* of them—past, present, and future.

EXERCISE **39** EXERCISE

Thinking about the Future

➤ Imagine your life five years from now if you were to continue using alcohol or other drugs. What will it be like? What will *you* be like?

_____

_____

_____

Selective Effort

As an addictive thinker, you will go to great trouble to get and use alcohol and other drugs. Just as you have plenty of energy when you need it for crime, you can go without food and sleep in your pursuit of getting high. However, when it comes to the day-to-day obligations of responsible living, you can't be bothered. You're too tired or too uninterested—or too busy getting high.

In part, this is because of your unwillingness to tolerate frustration. You often won't make the effort to try anything new or difficult because

1. If you fail, it might send you into the zero state.

2. You are afraid of all change, because growth and change threaten your using.

Your **selective effort** is part of the self-centeredness of your addictive thinking. You have the energy to fulfill your own pleasure desires, but not enough for others, including your children or other loved ones. You have the drive to score and use chemicals, but not to find and keep a job or finish school.

Magical Thinking and Codependency

Selective effort is more than self-centeredness. It is also a feature of your magical thinking. You tend to think that somehow things will work out without your having to make any effort. You think that somehow the trouble you've gotten yourself into will just go away. This magical thinking probably followed you into treatment.

It is also often the result of the codependent thinking of others. Since you are generally unwilling to make an effort, you try to get other people to make the effort for you. You want them to clean up all the messes you create with your chemical abuse, to do the work (effort) that is your responsibility, and to take care of you.

It is not surprising that addicts and alcoholics seek out codependents and that codependents seek out addicts and alcoholics. It is a powerful attraction. It is also an unhealthy relationship because each helps the other continue the thinking and behavior that is most destructive for them. Over time, codependents and addicts/alcoholics will (1) make themselves and each other miserable, and (2) eventually destroy their own and each other's lives.

EXERCISE **40** EXERCISE

Identifying Your Selective Efforts

➤ What obligations and responsibilities have you blown off to use chemicals?

_____

_____

_____

_____

_____

_____

_____

_____

Use of Deceit to Control

Both criminal and addictive thinkers believe they need to control others and situations. Addictive thinking says it is okay to use chemicals. When people challenge you on this, you want to control them. You believe that if you can control others and situations, you can continue with your chemical abuse.

As a criminal, you try to control others mainly through power tactics. As an addict, you try to control others mainly through lies. Since you are both a criminal and an addict, you use a mixture of both power and deceit, with each feeding into the other.

Using deceit to control means you will lie, cheat, steal, tell half-truths, and beg to get and continue using alcohol or other drugs. Denial is one form of deception. It is deceiving yourself about the harm of your chemical use. As an addict, however, you are also willing to lie to others as much as necessary in order to keep using. This kind of lying is different from denial—it is aggressive, self-centered, and extremely damaging to all your relationships.

The addictive thinking that uses deceit to control takes three directions:

1. You tend to become defensive when challenged about your chemical use, or you tell half-truths or make empty promises about quitting.

2. You must always be right about everything, since being wrong threatens your illusion of control. Therefore, you argue frequently and exaggerate to "win" arguments.

3. You will use this controlling power of deceit to keep others off balance to avoid challenges to your chemical use and maintain your source of supply.

EXERCISE **41** EXERCISE

The People Closest to You

➤ List the two most important people in your life. Then list three lies you told each of them in order to get, use, or get away with using alcohol or other drugs.

Name of person close to you: _____

Lies you told this person in order to use:

       1._____

       2._____

       3._____

Name of person close to you: _____

Lies you told this person in order to use:

       1._____

       2._____

       3._____

➤ What does it mean to you that you are willing to lie to the people who are most important in your life so you can get high?

_____

_____

_____

Seek Pleasure First

As a criminal thinker, you tend to seek excitement first and worry about consequences later (if at all). This impulsiveness is also a part of your addictive thinking. As an addictive thinker, you tend to **seek pleasure first**—the pleasure of getting high. You will seek this pleasure without regard for the serious physical, mental, and legal consequences that result. Even after your body begins to build a tolerance to your drug(s) of choice and it becomes more and more difficult to find a good high, you continue to seek, out of habit and physical craving, the drug-induced pleasure you once felt.

Addiction is a powerful mental and physical habit, driven by your memories of pleasurable drug experiences, your body's craving for the drug, and your unwillingness to tolerate discomfort. That means that when you feel frustrated, bored, anxious, or uncomfortable, your first thought is to relieve that discomfort as quickly as possible, and the fastest way you know to do that is with chemicals.

Obsession

An *obsession* is a powerful and persistent idea or feeling that demands almost all your attention.

Once you get the idea that you need to get high, little can stand in your way. You'll generally do whatever you need to do to find and use alcohol or other drugs. This is called *obsession,* and "seek pleasure first" thinking is the way your mind feeds your obsession with getting high.

One of the problems with your use of alcohol or other drugs and the thinking that leads you to seek pleasure first is that you identify happiness or feeling stress-free with being high.

A drug or alcohol high is a very temporary state.

Your body can't stand being intoxicated for long without breaking down. So when you are between highs or when your body develops *tolerance* and the high is less intense, it becomes very difficult for you to feel good. In this way, your "seek pleasure first" thinking actually leads you to more and more misery over time—and less and less pleasure. You become increasingly dissatisfied with everything and everybody, and you may find that even things that used to bring you joy no longer do.

EXERCISE **42** EXERCISE

Seeking Pleasure First

➤ List the main ways that you seek pleasure first when you are feeling bad or stressed. Be sure to list the behaviors, including chemical use (listing the specific drugs you'd choose), that you use to try to cover up uncomfortable feelings.

1. _____

2. _____

3. _____

4. _____

5. _____

6. _____

> ### Tolerance
>
> *Tolerance* is the body's increasing resistance to the effects of a drug that results from frequent use over time.

Ownership Stance

When you learned about criminal thinking, the **ownership stance** was summed up in two ideas:

- one-way property boundaries ("What's mine is mine, and what's yours is mine.")

- the idea that people are property ("She's mine, so she has to do as I say.")

With addictive thinking, this ownership stance and its disregard for the property rights of others comes from your obsession with getting high. Since you will do whatever it takes to feed your addiction, you mistakenly believe it is somehow okay for you to steal and to cheat others to get what you want most: drugs or alcohol. You also often treat others as if their purpose in life is to help you feel better—to get you drugs or alcohol, or provide you with sex, and to clean up the messes you make. This thinking turns people into property for you. It defeats the possibility of having a healthy relationship.

One of the ways you treat others as property is by expecting them to constantly behave in ways to better meet your needs. You have been unwilling, however, to make changes in yourself. You have decided somewhere along the road that the world should adjust to you rather than you adjusting to the world. That kind of ownership-stance thinking says the world is yours to use and violate in any way you wish to get what you want.

It's not hard to understand why people with this kind of thinking end up behind bars! Ownership-stance thinking separates you from others because you don't care about anyone else's real needs or rights. So you see, long before you were separated from society by being locked up, you had already separated yourself out from family, friends, and community with your ownership-stance thinking.

You have been unwilling to make changes in yourself.

The Property of Others

➤ List five things you stole to get drugs or alcohol.

1. _____

2. _____

3. _____

4. _____

5. _____

➤ Describe some of the thoughts you had to justify stealing these things.

_____

_____

_____

➤ Why do you think it's okay for you to take the property of others but not okay for others to take your property?

_____

_____

_____

People Are Not Property

Who are the people you used to help you get and use alcohol or other drugs? List two of them (by first name or initials only, if you choose). These are people you expect to provide excuses or to cover up for you. They are also friends, relatives, or acquaintances you have stolen from or ripped off in other ways (including dealers you bought drugs from and people you sold drugs to), and strangers you have cheated or robbed to buy drugs. (You may identify the strangers in any way that makes sense to you. For example, you could write, "The owner of the blue Buick" if, for example, you had stolen a CD player from a blue Buick in order to get money for drugs.)

➤ People you used   How you used them

1. _____   _____

   _____

   _____

2. _____   _____

   _____

   _____

➤ What would you have to do to live in a way that did not use others as if they were your property?

_____

How Criminal and Addictive Thinking Patterns Reinforce Each Other

Criminal and addictive thinking patterns are not only similar, they also feed each other. Criminal thinking patterns will lead you to addictive thinking patterns and vice versa. This means that if you commit a crime, the thinking involved will likely lead you to use alcohol or other drugs. If you use drugs or alcohol, the thinking that convinces you to do that will quite possibly lead you back to criminal activity. You begin to think you are invincible and invisible again—nothing can stop you and you won't get caught because you're too careful and slick. (See figure 10 on page 136.)

Drugs and alcohol lower your inhibitions and increase your impulsivity. *Inhibitions* are thought patterns that hold you in check and prevent you from doing something. A value system that says it's wrong to steal is an inhibition against stealing. The ability to understand another person's pain is an inhibition against hurting others. A belief that drugs or alcohol and criminal behavior are ruining your life and hurting your loved ones can be an inhibition against relapse and committing crimes in the future.

You are short on healthy inhibitions to begin with.

But when you lower them by getting drunk or high, you become even more impulsive and self-destructive.

Figure 10
HOW CRIMINAL AND ADDICTIVE THINKING DRIVE EACH OTHER

ADDICTIVE THINKING

Controls with Deceit
manipulates with lies
undermines and confuses
passive-aggressive
abusive
cheats and cons

Self-Obsessed
self is shameful
self-pitying
loner
unique
resentful

Irresponsible
false promises
sexually selfish
impulsive
unreliable
denies facts
ducks obligations

False Pride
self is special
grandiose
sentimental
cynical
fear of death
self is smarter
intolerant

Pleasure Focused
craves sensuality
instant gratification
lustful
low discomfort tolerance

Rigid
self-righteous
defensive
need to be right
perfectionistic
judgmental
absolutist

CRIMINAL THINKING

Controls with Power
manipulates with threats
undermines and confuses
intimidates
abusive
cheats and cons

Self-Centered
self is nothing (zero)
self is victim
loner
unique
entitled

Irresponsible
lack of effort
sexually predatory
impulsive
unreliable
distorts facts
refuses obligations

Criminal Pride
self is good person
extremely high self-image
sentimental
cynical
fear of humiliation
self is tougher
quick temper

Excitement Focused
craves thrills
instant gratification
power hungry
low boredom tolerance

Concrete
self-righteous
close-minded
need to be on top
perfectionistic
all or nothing
absolutist

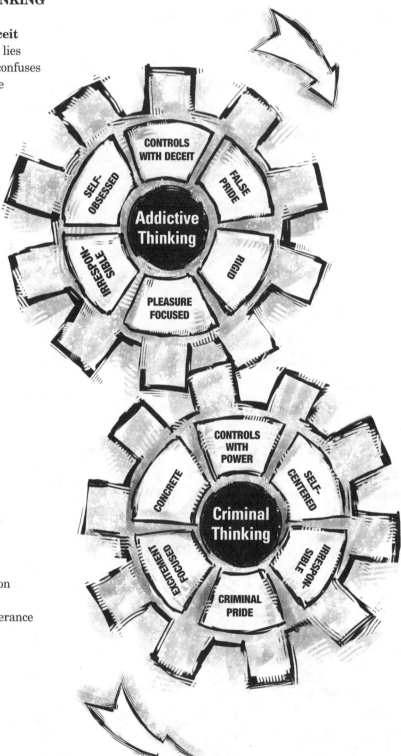

If you have not already done so, you are now ready to start identifying your addictive thinking patterns and alternative thoughts and adding them to your Thinking Reports. The Thinking Report exercise is found on page 49.

■

Core Beliefs

Remember, core beliefs are those generalized beliefs or "rules" that are true throughout our thinking and applied to almost all situations. They are the very basic assumptions we make about the world, others, and ourselves. They are so automatic that we often don't even stop to think about them. Core beliefs make up what we believe about reality and our self-identity—what we hold as important or meaningful, and what options or choices we see as available to us.

Core beliefs are the thoughts behind our thinking.

They are the thoughts that lead us from "That person makes me mad" to "He deserves to be hit," or from "I like the looks of that car" to "Therefore it's okay for me to steal it." Or they are the thoughts behind the thinking that takes us from "I should never have to feel bad" to "Therefore it's all right to use alcohol or drugs because I deserve to feel good." Your beliefs determine how you justify and explain your behavior. They are the story you tell yourself and others that makes it okay for you to rob, steal, assault, and use alcohol and drugs despite the consequences to yourself and your relationships.

Not all your core beliefs are distorted. Some of them help to protect you. They also help you to consider the needs and safety of others. Healthy core beliefs don't cause harm to others—they don't create victims.

Identifying Your Core Beliefs

➤ Write down the first thing that comes to your mind:

1. The world is _____

2. Other people are _____

3. Other people should try to _____

4. I try to be _____

5. The world would be better if _____

_____

6. The best way to get what you want is to _____

_____

7. I deserve _____

_____

8. If people try to stop me from getting what I want, then

_____

_____

"The Little Engine That Could"

Core beliefs are the thoughts behind your thinking. Remember the children's story called *The Little Engine That Could*? The story is about a small train engine that is asked to pull many freight cars filled with toys and candy across a mountain. The train's first engine had broken down and no other engines were willing to do the work. Though no one thought the little engine was powerful enough for the job, it volunteered to try. It started out by saying to itself, "I think I can. I think I can." It kept saying "I think I can" as it picked up speed and as it began the long, hard climb up the mountain. It continued to say it until it finally reached the top and could begin the easy trip down the other side.

What does this simple child's tale have to do with core beliefs? Let's work backward:

Question: What was the behavior?
Answer:　Pulling the train over the mountain.

Question: What was the thought behind the behavior?
Answer:　I think I can.

Question: What was the core belief behind the thought?
Answer:　I believe that, with effort and determination, I can do more than others think I'm capable of doing.

Your core beliefs support your thinking, just like the rocks and earth underneath the ground support the world you live in. You don't see them, but they are there. You can also think of core beliefs as the framework of a big building—the girders and beams that make up the skeleton of the building—that you don't see but that keep the whole building from collapsing.

The same is true of your core beliefs. They are so automatic that we are often not even aware of their impact on our thinking and behavior. But by looking at your thinking distortions and criminal and addictive thinking, you can begin to identify which of your core beliefs cause harm to others—and to yourself.

Following are some examples of core beliefs.

View of the world:

- It's a dog-eat-dog world.

- The world should be just and fair.

- People get what they deserve out of life.

View of others:

- Everyone is out for themselves.

- Get them before they get you.

- Treat others as you'd want to be treated.

- Others are here to meet my needs, or at least they should stay out of my way.

- People are basically good.

View of self:

- Since I am special, I deserve special treatment.

- I can make a positive difference in people's lives.

- Rules aren't for me; I am entitled to break the rules.

- If people knew the real me, they would reject me.

- My feelings are always correct.

Based on your core beliefs, you develop certain strategies to make things go according to your thinking. But you—like most people—generally look at the world *through* your core beliefs. You seldom look *at* them. And you believe that everyone else in the world looks at things the way you do. For example, you probably think

- Everybody in your situation would have done the things you did.

- Everybody uses because everybody in *your* world uses.

- If everybody had as hard a life as you, they'd commit crimes, too.

Sometimes things happen that go against what you believe are "just the way things are." When this is the case, you are much more likely to change or distort that information to fit what you already believe. Again, that's true for most people, not just criminals.

Criminals, however, have core beliefs that allow for and justify criminal behavior.

So when you believe it's a dog-eat-dog world and someone does something nice for you, you automatically think that person must be trying to con you. When people make you angry, you tell yourself you are justified in beating them up because "they asked for it" or "they should have known better" or "they simply got what they deserved."

A problem that many people, including criminals, have with their core beliefs is that they think everyone has the same core beliefs that they have. It's wrong to assume that our core beliefs are the same as everyone else's. Many of your life's conflicts happened because you tried to insist that everyone else shares your core beliefs.

One of the basic goals of treatment is to get you to look at, and question, some of your core beliefs.

One of the basic goals of treatment is to get you to look at, and question, some of your core beliefs. You need to look at the "rules" that you apply automatically across different situations. Doing so will cause you to react and behave in ways that create problems for yourself and others. As a result, this examination is a very difficult thing to do.

How Core Beliefs Lead to Thinking and Behavior

➤ Write your current offense below in the far right-hand column. Then review your answers to the questions in exercise 45. Use those answers as a guide to the core beliefs that seem to have a connection to your current offense. List them below in the far left-hand column.

In the middle column, write a thought that could come out of each of the core beliefs that would lead to committing your current offense.

Core beliefs   Specific thoughts

1. _____   _____

   _____   _____

2. _____   _____

   _____   _____   _____
                                                  current offense

3. _____   _____   (behavior)

   _____   _____

The crime is the behavior. It resulted from specific thoughts like the ones you described in this exercise. The thoughts came out of your core beliefs about the world, others, and yourself.

Exercise 46 helped you start to become aware of your core beliefs. Yet it will take you much more time and effort to challenge those beliefs. Seeing what kinds of issues come up again and again in your Thinking Reports and what your thoughts are leading up to those situations can help your thinking become more deliberate and less reactive.

If you have not already done so, you are now ready to start identifying the core beliefs (the thoughts behind your thoughts) that operate behind your criminal and addictive thinking patterns, and to start adding core beliefs to your Thinking Reports. You are also ready to begin trying to think of replacement core beliefs—new beliefs—that might work better for you in recovery. Adding new beliefs may lead you to healthier, more rewarding thoughts and outcomes. Turn back to the Thinking Report on page 49 to add this information.

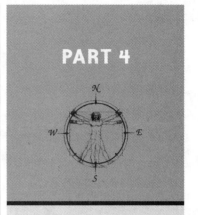

Learning to Think about Your Behaviors

We've discussed thinking distortions, criminal and addictive thinking patterns, and core beliefs, and we've shown how all these can lead to irresponsible behavior. Remember, your *behavior* is the result of your *thinking*. Earlier in this workbook, you explored your habits of thinking. Now you'll look at some of your habits of behavior that resulted from that thinking.

Behavior can be responsible, irresponsible (legal, but potentially damaging to you or others), or criminal (violating others in ways society prohibits by law). Since you are reading this in a treatment program behind bars, you have seriously broken the law at least once and perhaps many, many more times.

In fact, the odds are that you have done so much irresponsible behavior, both criminal and noncriminal, that you have developed patterns of behavior. These behavior strategies have worked well for you in manipulating, intimidating, controlling, and violating others. You have used these behaviors so often and so consistently that they have become habits for you. These habits of criminal and addictive behavior are called *tactics*. Because they are habits, you use these criminal and addictive tactics in almost everything you do. You are probably using them in this treatment program.

The use of criminal and addictive tactics is a habit of behavior you will have to change in order to recover from both your criminality and your alcohol and drug use. To change these habits and recover, you will need to understand the thinking behind the tactics—why you do what you do.

Tactics

Tactics are planned behavior strategies and approaches intended to achieve a goal.

Criminal and Addictive Tactics

You use criminal and addictive tactics as a survival mechanism. You use them to avoid restrictions. You use them to get what you think you want. You use them to get people off your case or to avoid being held accountable for your behavior. And you also use them to avoid feeling put down or disrespected by others.

Who Uses Tactics?

Who uses tactics? Pretty much everybody. Generals, sales-people, parents, athletes, teachers, business managers, therapists, and others use tactics. Tactics are simply behaviors that are meant to get things done.

When responsible people use responsible tactics, they are intending to accomplish something helpful and worth-while for themselves, their families, or their communities. The key is that they are not willing to use tactics in a way that violates the rights of others.

When irresponsible people use irresponsible tactics, they are trying to get something for themselves without earning it. They hide their true motives to take advantage of others and avoid responsibility.

When criminals use criminal tactics, they are trying to avoid being held accountable. They want to promote their criminal and addictive life—to get what they think they are entitled to or to avoid the feelings of zero state.

How You Use Tactics

Criminal and addictive tactics are divided into these three types of strategies:

1. avoidance strategies

2. diversion strategies

3. aggression strategies

You use *avoidance strategies* to escape responsibility, to keep a low profile so you won't have to put out effort or be exposed, and to manipulate others to get what you want.

You use *diversion strategies* to confuse others, to direct attention away from yourself or from the important issues, and to avoid exposure by keeping those around you distracted and focused on other things.

You use *aggression strategies* to attack, intimidate, and undermine the efforts of others. You actively try to create chaos by stirring up conflict, resentment, and other hard feelings.

Your main goals with aggression strategies are

- avoiding exposure and keeping others on the defensive
- getting what you want, especially when you believe that other people are getting in your way
- responding when you think you have been provoked or made to look bad

The use of all three types of criminal and addictive tactics is the source of your feelings of criminal excitement and power. These strategies fuel your anger, resentment, and sense of entitlement. They help you deny the need for change by helping you deny your criminal and addictive thinking patterns, thinking distortions, and faulty core beliefs. They prevent you from setting goals for change.

Most criminals and addicts use all the tactics but in different orders. For example, you may prefer avoidance strategies, but if you run through all the avoidance tactics in a situation and they aren't working, you may flip over to diversion strategies. If those don't work, you'll try aggression strategies, and so on. Each person has his favorite tactics that he uses most often, but every criminal and addict is ready and willing to use any tactic that works in a situation.

For all these reasons, it is important that you understand one thing about your habits of behavior:

> As a criminal and addictive thinker, you cannot make progress in treatment until you give up the excitement and power of using these criminal and addictive tactics and committing crimes or getting high.

And that has to start right now, in treatment. The first step in dealing with your use of criminal tactics is to name the tactics you use and learn to see them in your behavior. Then you can begin adding your tactics to your Thinking Reports.

Why is this just the first step? Because although understanding is crucial to change, it is not change. As your understanding of your use of tactics grows, you will begin the real work of recovery: letting go of old irresponsible habits of living and substituting new, responsible ones *(new behaviors)* that will help you get along better in the world.

Avoidance Strategies

Here are the seven basic criminal and addictive tactics you use to get away with irresponsible thinking and behavior by avoidance:

1. lying by omission or commission (passive and active lying)

2. being deliberately vague

3. staying silent to avoid notice

4. false compliance

    a. compliance without commitment

    b. passive resistance compliance

5. playing dumb

6. selective memory and attention

7. minimizing (trivializing)

TACTIC 1:

Lying by Omission or Commission

Lying by omission or commission means misleading others by hiding the truth or telling half-truths (lying by omission, or passive lying) or misleading them by telling them things that are not true (lying by commission, or active lying). One is not better or worse than the other: a lie is a lie. You use lies to avoid getting caught, to hold power over others (withholding information can be powerful), to avoid accountability, and to continue your lifestyle.

You are lying by *omission* when you

- believe only you know what is important to disclose and what isn't

- disclose only the information that benefits you while withholding other important information, often by leaving out important details

- say "I don't know" or "I don't remember" when pressured for details; you do this as a way of avoiding accountability or an uncomfortable situation when in fact you *do* know

- twist facts and distort situations by shifting the emphasis onto minor facts while omitting crucial parts of the story

You are lying by *commission* when you

- make up stories to cover yourself and put others off the track

- deny to yourself or others what you know to be true

- believe that the truth works against your best interests and act accordingly

- distort, invent, turn upside down, or deny facts

TACTIC 2:

Being Deliberately Vague

Being deliberately vague means distorting the truth by fudging details, being intentionally uncertain of times and places, and trying to answer questions with wishy-washy generalities. Frequently claiming "I don't know" or "I can't remember" is one way of being deliberately vague. You use this tactic so you don't get pinned down. It's another way you avoid accountability and refuse to make a commitment to recovery. You think that vague statements will be enough to get people off your back without your having to confront your thinking and behavior and make changes. And you think that if others don't call you on it, then that's their problem. At least you didn't have to lie to them, and you can still tell yourself you're an honest person (even though you're not).

You are being deliberately vague when you

- talk and talk and talk about yourself without ever revealing any relevant information

- edit stories to give a false general impression that you were the victim instead of the victimizer

- try to conceal something through your careful choice of words and phrases

- avoid giving direct answers to direct questions

- use empty, nondisclosing phrases

- say "I'll think about it" when you're pinned down, though you never bring it up again. When you're challenged, you say, "I forgot"

TACTIC 3:

Staying Silent to Avoid Notice

Staying silent to avoid notice could also be called "trying to fly under the radar." Again, you try to avoid being challenged by "blending into the woodwork." You hope that if you keep your mouth shut, everyone will ignore you and you can cruise through life—and your treatment program—without putting in any effort.

The purpose of silence is to maintain your criminal and addictive lifestyle through secrecy. It is also a way to control others and to keep others at a distance. Sometimes you use silence to buy yourself time to size up another person so you can figure out how to manipulate him or her.

You use silence as a criminal tactic when you

- say, "I don't know and I don't care"

- refuse to listen or participate

- say, "I just can't explain it" while shrugging or sighing

- say, "Nothing happened"

- say, "I don't have anything to say. They said it all"

TACTIC 4:

False Compliance

Like lying, *false compliance* shows up in two ways: compliance without commitment and passive resistance.

In your treatment program, *compliance without commitment* is an attempt to con the therapists into thinking that you're doing the work and making changes, while in fact you're just saying what you think they want to hear so they won't challenge you. You say the "right" things to staff, but you don't really mean what you say. You think that if you can keep the therapists happy, they won't notice that you're really just putting in time.

You've also probably used compliance without commitment with your family, your spouse or partner, and an employer to get them off your case.

Passive resistance is a type of false compliance where you do the absolute minimum to get by. Not one little bit more. You don't actively fight the system, but you're determined not to give in to it by looking at your thinking and behavior and making changes.

You are using false compliance as a criminal tactic when you

- try to "score points" by saying the right thing or by doing the right thing just one time

- tell different people different versions of your thoughts and experiences depending on what you think they want to hear or what will make you look good in their eyes

- promise to change by saying, "I'll never do it again"

- claim to have changed by doing something right once

- try to convince therapists that you've completed treatment and learned everything you need to stay sober and crime free when in fact you're just restless, bored, and seeking excitement

- claim to have had a miraculous transformation

- say yes without meaning it

- fake interest with intense concentration, eye contact, and nodding head

- say, "I guess so," "You're right," or "It makes sense to me," when in fact you don't agree or it doesn't make sense to you or you simply don't care

You are using false compliance as a criminal tactic when you promise to change by saying, "I'll never do it again."

TACTIC 5:

Playing Dumb

Playing dumb is an act you put on to try to convince others that you are too fragile, helpless, or stupid to be responsible so that they'll let you off the hook. Or you may tell staff you'd really like to look at those issues if only you had an idea of what they are talking about. Again, you try to fool others into thinking you're just not capable of making a responsible effort or don't understand what it is they are asking you to look at. You use this tactic to escape having to work at change.

You use playing dumb as a criminal tactic when you

- pretend to have less education or a lower reading ability than you really have in order to get out of making an effort

- frequently complain, "I didn't understand the question" or "I don't know what you are talking about" without making an effort to understand

- look blankly when you are confronted or challenged, as if you're incapable of understanding the situation and giving a meaningful response

- make simplistic or off-base comments in order to appear lost and confused

- exaggerate or make up mental or physical health problems to excuse your lack of compliance or effort

- complain about having too much to do or that the work is too hard

TACTIC 6:

Selective Memory and Attention

Selective memory and attention is yet another tactic for avoiding accountability. You remember only what's convenient to remember, so you won't be challenged or exposed. You also pay attention only to what you want to hear. You tune out anything that would make you uncomfortable about your criminal and addictive thinking and behavior.

You use selective memory and attention as a criminal tactic when you

- put off obligations by saying, "I forgot" or "I'm too busy right now" or "I'll do it later," even though you have little intention of ever following through

- ignore anything that challenges your thinking or lifestyle

- have little patience with ideas that don't fit in with yours

- believe the assignments and lectures in treatment don't apply to you—sometimes even before you've really looked at them

- twist statements that challenge your thinking around in your mind until you mistakenly believe they actually support your thinking

- pretend to listen by looking at the speaker and nodding or agreeing, while you are really thinking about other things that are more satisfying to you

- try to shift the responsibility for your lack of attention by claiming the speaker wasn't being clear

TACTIC 7:

Minimizing (Trivializing)

Minimizing, or *trivializing,* begins in your mind as a way to block out thoughts of your wrongdoing and deny the full extent of the harm you have caused others. Instead of denying what you did, you try to make it seem trivial or less significant than it is. You minimize when you

- play down the importance of a situation

- view your offenses as less serious than others do

- minimize the harm of your actions when you are held accountable

- claim you didn't *intend* to cause so much harm

Here are some examples of minimizing:

- "I just got into a little trouble."

- "It was a mistake—I was just playing a prank."

- "I caught a case" or "I found myself in a situation."

- "I only dealt a little crack. It's not like I used it."

- "I only did it a few times." (When in fact you've done it seven, eight, or more times, which would be "many" or "a lot," not "a few.")

■

You have probably used all of these avoidance tactics at one time or another. In fact, you probably are using many of them in your treatment program right now.

Identifying Your Avoidance Strategies

➤ Choose two tactics from the list of avoidance strategies that you used *before* you were incarcerated this most recent time. Give a detailed example of how you used each tactic. Include what you hoped would happen when you used those tactics (how you hoped others would react, what you hoped to avoid, or what advantage you thought you'd gain).

1. Avoidance tactic

_____

How you used this tactic and what you hoped to gain by it

_____

_____

_____

2. Avoidance tactic

_____

How you used this tactic and what you hoped to gain by it

_____

_____

_____

Avoidance Strategies

1. lying by omission or commission (passive and active lying)

2. being deliberately vague

3. staying silent to avoid notice

4. false compliance
   a. compliance without commitment
   b. passive resistance compliance

5. playing dumb

6. selective memory and attention

7. minimizing (trivializing)

EXAMPLE:

Avoidance tactic:
Being deliberately vague

How you used this tactic and what you hoped to gain by it:

When I was out doing a job—burglaries or whatever—and my wife would ask where I'd been, I'd just say I'd picked up some day work with some guys. If she pushed for details, I'd get mad and accuse her of not trusting me. I wanted her to back off so she wouldn't find out I was doing crime again and get pissed off at me.

➤ Now write down two avoidance strategies you have used in treatment and give an example of how you've used each one. Explain what you hoped to get out of using that strategy each time.

1. Avoidance tactic

_____

How you used this tactic and what you hoped to gain by it

_____

_____

_____

2. Avoidance tactic

_____

How you used this tactic and what you hoped to gain by it

_____

_____

_____

Diversion Strategies

The second category of criminal and addictive tactics is *diversion strategies*. Again, diversion strategies are the tactics you use to confuse others, to misdirect attention away from yourself or from the most important issues, and to avoid exposure by keeping those around you off balance and distracted. You use diversion strategies for the same reasons you use all other tactics:

to help you continue an irresponsible way of thinking and living.

The seven basic tactics you use to divert attention from the work you need to do to change and the things you need to be accountable for are listed below. (We've numbered them 8–14 to pick up where we left off with the avoidance strategies.)

8. pointing out the faults of others

9. magnifying (exaggerating significance)

10. deliberately trying to confuse

11. quibbling over words

12. introducing irrelevant issues

13. discussing smokescreen issues

14. using self-shaming to avoid responsibility

TACTIC 8:

Pointing Out the Faults of Others

One way you divert attention from your wrongdoings and from your criminal and addictive thinking is to *point out the faults and failures of others.* As long as you can keep the focus on someone else—"I'm not as bad as *he* is; *he's* the one who has got a lot of work to do"—you think you can get away with not taking responsibility for what you need to change. You point out the faults of your peers, your family, staff, administrators, the commissioner of corrections, the president of the United States—it doesn't matter who—because the purpose is to keep the focus on anyone other than you.

You are pointing out the faults of others as a criminal tactic when you

- make a big issue over a mistake made by staff
- get overly involved in giving critical feedback in group to peers in order to use up all the time and not allow the group an opportunity to give you critical feedback
- talk behind people's backs (backbiting) in order to get others focused on everyone else's shortcomings and issues and not yours

TACTIC 9:

Magnifying (Exaggerating Significance)

Magnifying, or *exaggerating the significance,* of minor issues is a tactic you use to justify your behavior or divert attention from your own issues. Stirring up debate or conflict over small matters can also give you a sense of control and some easy thrills. You use this tactic just to see how far you can push somebody (giving you a feeling of power), to distract others, and to put others on the defensive. You take little things and blow them out of proportion.

You are using the magnifying criminal tactic as a diversion when you

- point out the small inconsistencies of others and then dwell on them

- try to start conflicts between peers or between staff and peers over minor issues

- keep the attention on others in the group by arguing with them about what they've shared, rather than just giving appropriate feedback

- go on and on about something good you've done or all the progress you've made in order to keep the focus off the work you still have to do

- exaggerate the fault of the other person in a conflict in order to make your role in the conflict seem less significant than it really is

TACTIC 10:

Deliberately Trying to Confuse

As a criminal and addictive thinker, you will sometimes *try to confuse* others in order to get the upper hand. Keeping others confused is a way of maintaining your sense of power and diverting attention from yourself and the important issues at hand. This tactic once again reveals how little respect you have for the truth. In fact, you use this tactic in part because you mistakenly believe the truth is your enemy.

You are deliberately trying to confuse others when you

- offer inconsistent versions of an event

- jump around quickly from point to point

- speak so fast that others can't follow your words

- speak so slowly that others can't maintain interest in what you're saying

- use street language, personal slang, double-talk, or fancy words so that others won't be sure what you're really saying (in such cases, you are usually saying nothing)

- misquote others by twisting the meaning of their words or claiming they said things they never said

- when challenged on a discrepancy or inconsistency, claim the listener misunderstood, thereby shifting the burden to the other person

- stop in the middle of a story, admit you were lying, and claim you're now going to tell the whole truth, when in fact you have no such intention

TACTIC 11:

Quibbling over Words

Quibbling over words is a way to not only divert attention from more important things but also to make yourself appear smart in front of peers or staff. By disputing the meaning of words or phrases someone else uses rather than trying to understand that person, you take control of the conversation by knocking it off track.

You are quibbling over words when you

- say, "What you say is incorrect—that phrase means [this] and not [that]"

- argue over the exact language used rather than trying to clarify the exact meaning intended

- misquote someone and then make a big deal claiming your version is correct

- if a staff member asks you if you know anything about the assault out on the yard, you say, "I didn't see the assault," even though you may know exactly who did it and why (you just didn't see the actual assault)

TACTIC 12:

Introducing Irrelevant Issues

Another tactic you use to divert attention away from your-self and your criminal and addictive behavior is *introducing irrelevant issues.* You may try to direct discussion toward things that interest you, such as cars, sports, politics, or music—anything to avoid discussing your crimes and your criminal and addictive thinking patterns. You may intro-duce your personal history—family troubles or social dis-advantages growing up—to distract others from your recent behavior. Or you may introduce race, one of the most sensitive issues in this society and especially in prison (as you know). As a criminal and an addict, you use race in order to justify, excuse, or keep the focus away from your behavior. And yes, race can be and is used as a diver-sion strategy by people of *all* races—including yours.

The fact is, your interests, your personal history, and race *are* important issues, and they deserve thought and discussion, but only in an appropriate way and time. Using them in any way to avoid looking at and changing your criminal and addictive thinking and behavior is introducing irrelevant issues. Like all the other tactics, its purpose is to allow you to keep thinking and living the way you have been—to avoid change.

You are introducing irrelevant issues when you

- use race to present yourself as a victim, thereby refusing to admit how you have been the victimizer

- charge racism when you don't get your own way or when your other tactics don't work and others continue to confront you

- constantly talk about your rights in order to avoid talking about your "wrongs"

- justify your crimes and alcohol and drug use with sad stories of how hard you've had it in life. Even if the stories are true, they don't excuse your personal behavior and choices

- try to start arguments about other subjects when you are confronted by family, therapists, or peers
- blame your behavior choices on social injustice

TACTIC 13:

Discussing Smokescreen Issues

Smokescreen issues are slightly different from irrelevant issues. Smokescreen issues may be treatment issues that you use at inappropriate times in order to avoid disclosure. For example, you focus on some family issues in chemical dependency group or on your addiction in the family group.

Another form of using smokescreen issues is picking just one issue and keeping the discussion about your behavior as it relates to that issue at all times. If you have been diagnosed as depressed, you may talk about nothing else except your depression. It becomes a smokescreen issue when you use it to keep attention away from your criminal and addictive thinking and behavior. You say that if only you could take care of the depression, then you could really take advantage of the program and change. It's not that your depression is irrelevant to your thinking and behavior, it's that it is only one part of it.

You are using smokescreen issues when you

- keep writing the same Thinking Reports over and over

- discuss treatment issues in the wrong group or at the wrong time to keep from focusing on the subject at hand

- introduce physical or mental health problems just to excuse you from treatment work

TACTIC 14:

Using Self-Shaming to Avoid Responsibility

For those who prefer the diversion tactics, *using self-shaming to avoid responsibility* is often a last resort. When you are backed into a corner, you try to avoid taking a hard look at your behavior and thinking by shaming yourself publicly. You think that if you beat yourself up enough in front of peers and therapists, they'll let you off the hook. Or you may continually claim that your unresolved shame issues must be addressed before you can do the work at hand.

This diversion tactic should not be confused with your legitimate issues. The important difference between the two is the *reason* you are bringing up your feelings of shame. Are you just trying to distract attention or are you sincerely asking for help? Asking for help with shame issues is appropriate—at the right time and with the right person. Treatment, however, is not about shame. It's about *change*.

Self-shaming can be just another way to keep the attention of others off the fact that you still haven't done the work. Your self-shaming may be genuine or it may just be an act. It doesn't matter. Either way, you still haven't looked hard at your thinking and behavior and disclosed it to the group. You still haven't tried to make changes in how you think and live. You still haven't gotten honest.

You use self-shaming when you

- admit to and dwell on one crime or behavior to hide more serious ones

- talk and talk about what an awful person you are to get pity from others

Identifying Your Diversion Strategies

➤ Choose two tactics that you have used from the list of diversion strategies. Give a detailed example of how you used each tactic. Include what you hoped would happen when you used those tactics (how you hoped others would react, what you hoped to divert attention from, or what advantage you thought you'd gain).

1. Diversion tactic

   _____

   How did you use this tactic and what did you hope to gain by it?

   _____

   _____

   _____

2. Diversion tactic

   _____

   How did you use this tactic and what did you hope to gain by it?

   _____

   _____

   _____

Diversion Strategies

8. pointing out the faults of others

9. magnifying (exaggerating significance)

10. deliberately trying to confuse

11. quibbling over words

12. introducing irrelevant issues

13. discussing smokescreen issues

14. using self-shaming to avoid responsibility

EXAMPLE:

Diversion tactic:
Magnifying
(exaggerating significance)

How did you use this tactic and what did you hope to gain by it?
When my cellmate took a pen from me without asking and I caught him using it working on one of the workbook exercises, I made a big deal about him disrespecting me and my property. But the thing is, I didn't really give a damn about the pen. I was just trying to rile things up and put it on him so I'd look good.

Aggression Strategies

To review, you use *aggression strategies* to attack, intimidate, and undermine the legitimate efforts of others. You actively try to create chaos through stirring up conflict, resentment, and other hard feelings. You take on the victim role, saying that others provoked you or at least didn't get out of your way. You tell yourself, then, that they are just getting what they deserve. You also try to make others fear you so they won't challenge your addictive and criminal thinking. Again, your main goals with aggression strategies are getting what you want, avoiding exposure and the zero state by keeping others on the defensive, and responding when you think you have been provoked or made to look bad.

The seven basic aggression strategies that criminals use to prevent others from confronting their thinking and behavior are listed below.

(We've numbered them 15–21 to pick up where we left off with the diversion strategies.)

15. arguing
16. using threatening words or behaviors (veiled or overt)
17. raging
18. sarcasm and teasing
19. splitting staff
20. creating chaos
21. attention seeking

TACTIC 15:

Arguing

Arguing is an aggressive criminal and addictive tactic you use to keep your distance from others and to get what you want. It is yet another strategy you have for protecting your criminal and addictive way of life.

Arguing turns a ***dialogue*** of ideas into just a war of words. Nobody learns anything new in an argument because arguing is not about learning, it's about winning. That means its only purpose is to pump up your ego and humiliate the other person.

You are using arguing as an aggressive criminal and addictive tactic when you

- raise your voice in a discussion, feel the adrenaline rush of battle, and focus only on proving the other person wrong

- refuse to listen to or think about what others are saying

- turn meanings around and attack (with words) the points of view of others

- try to turn the tables when you are confronted for not living up to an agreement by arguing that the other person misunderstood the agreement

- use anger and intensity to try to overpower others in a discussion and avoid having to look honestly at your deeper thoughts and fears

- turn conversations (dialogues) into power struggles and insist on having the last word

TACTIC 16:

Using Threatening Words or Behaviors (Veiled or Direct)

You use two types of *threatening words and behaviors* to try to control others, *veiled* and *direct*. Veiled threats are more hidden. They may include intimidating body language, such as threatening stares ("mean mugging") or flexing muscles in your arms and neck or clenching your fists. Veiled threats could also be vague statements that suggest "something bad" might happen to someone.

Direct threatening words and behaviors are more out in the open and include physical intimidation or statements of intent to cause harm. You use them to reinforce your feelings of superiority and entitlement and to avoid putdowns.

You are using veiled threatening words and behaviors when you

- say, "If I wasn't in this program trying to get healthy, you wouldn't be talking like that for long"

- say, "Where are the grievance forms?"

- say, "Remember what you did last weekend? It would be unfortunate if the staff found out"

- say, "My brothers ain't going to like that"

- use "mean mugging" or other threatening body language

You are using direct threatening words and behaviors when you

- hit or push someone

- say, "You're a dead man—my brothers will see to that"

- stand over someone flexing your muscles, staring, and making fists

- physically back someone down

- prey on the vulnerabilities of others

- curse at others

You use threatening words and behaviors to reinforce your feelings of superiority and to avoid putdowns.

TACTIC 17:

Raging

You use *raging* as a tactic when you let yourself go wild with anger—yelling and screaming and threatening and throwing things (behavior guaranteed to put you in seg or get you thrown out of the program). You also use raging when you suggest that if someone doesn't leave you alone, you could explode at any time. You tell "war stories" about all the people you have beat up because you have a short fuse and can't control yourself. Raging is another way you attempt to control others—by making them keep their distance and making them afraid of you. You believe that someone who is afraid of you won't confront your criminal and addictive ways.

You are raging when you

- lose all control in anger and become wild and destructive

- make others believe you *could* lose all control and fly into a rage at any time, so they'd better treat you very carefully

TACTIC 18:

Sarcasm and Teasing

Sarcasm is sharp and mean-spirited language used to make others look stupid or worthless. You use it as an aggression tactic to build yourself up by putting others down. Sarcasm and *teasing* are strategies designed to control others by keeping them on the defensive. As with all aggression strategies, they are efforts to make you feel powerful and warn others to keep their distance.

You are using sarcasm and teasing when you

- are sharply critical and unforgiving when others slip up

- pick on others for their appearance or the way they talk

- try to embarrass, demean, or make fun of another with little digs or insults

- say, "I guess you wouldn't happen to know that . . ." in order to make someone look dumb

TACTIC 19:

Splitting Staff

Splitting staff is a common aggressive tactic used by people who are incarcerated and in treatment programs. Splitting staff is a variation of the old military strategy "divide and conquer." By trying to pit one staff member against another, you hope to decrease their authority and effectiveness and increase your influence and power. Lost in this game, of course, is any hope of your doing the treatment work and making the changes that could keep you out of prison and help you live responsibly in the world.

You are splitting staff when you

- tell one staff member, "You really understand me, unlike those other therapists"

- attack a staff member by saying, "You're the worst therapist here. All the others are better than you"

- twist stories around so one staff member will think that another is being unfair to you

- tell different versions of an incident to different staff members to try to put them in conflict

- go "staff shopping" until one finally gives you the answer you want

You may also use the splitting staff tactic to split your peer group. You are splitting peer groups when you

- say, "I can do treatment with him, but not with *that* guy"

- try to purposely ruin someone's reputation by spreading rumors

TACTIC 20:

Creating Chaos

You are *creating chaos* as a tactic when you use a combination of other tactics to cause a constant disruption of programs, groups, exercises, and life on the unit. You may be spreading rumors (even about yourself) while you try to split staff, attack peers behind their backs, threaten peers in and out of group, accuse others of misunderstanding you, change your story depending on who is listening, argue over everything, and demand your rights. The idea is to keep the staff so busy dealing with the messes you make that the program grinds to a halt.

You create chaos in order to

- avoid working on your thinking and behavior and making changes

- get pleasure from the feeling of power and control it gives you

- feel like a big shot, that no treatment program is ever going to change *you*

TACTIC 21:

Attention Seeking

Attention seeking becomes an aggressive tactic anytime it disrupts the efforts of others to work the treatment program. Often you use bizarre or shocking behaviors or disclosures to stir things up.

You are using attention seeking as an aggressive criminal and addictive tactic when you

- threaten to quit the program

- do outrageous things to stand out and grab the group's attention or to intentionally upset people

- dress to show off a gang tattoo or muscles

- walk around like you are big, bad, and nationwide

- aggressively refuse to comply with staff

Identifying Your Aggression Strategies

➤ Choose two tactics that you have used from the list of aggression strategies. Give a detailed example of how you used each tactic. Include what you hoped would happen when you used those tactics (how you hoped others would react, what you hoped to divert attention from, or what advantage you thought you'd gain).

1. Aggression tactic

   _____

   How did you use this tactic and what did you hope to gain by it?

   _____

   _____

   _____

2. Aggression tactic

   _____

   How did you use this tactic and what did you hope to gain by it?

   _____

   _____

   _____

Aggression Strategies

15. arguing
16. using threatening words or behaviors (veiled or overt)
17. raging
18. sarcasm and teasing
19. splitting staff
20. creating chaos
21. attention seeking

EXAMPLE:

Aggression tactic:
Sarcasm and teasing

How did you use this tactic and what did you hope to gain by it?
When X asked what "strategy" meant, I laughed out loud and said to the guy next to me, "They must not of gotten to that in the second grade," and I said it loud enough so several people around me could hear. I wanted to make X look like an idiot and make me look smart. I did it because it felt good to put him down. It also showed everybody I'm a hardass, so let me be.

Switching Strategies

As a criminal and addictive thinker, you have particular tactics you prefer. You may especially like aggression strategies because they seem to give you what you want most. Or you may be the type who thinks lying low—using avoidance strategies—is the most effective way of keeping people off your back and allowing you to continue your criminal and addictive lifestyle.

When your favorite tactics don't work, however, you will readily switch to another type to get what you want: power, control, and avoiding responsibility, accountability, and change. For example, some criminals and addicts who use avoidance strategies and appear passive will switch over immediately to aggressive, threatening tactics in a situation as soon as they figure out that the avoidance tactics aren't working. Understanding how you use all these tactics will help you begin to stop them and to find new behaviors that are more effective in getting along in the world.

Sometimes you may work your way "up the ladder," starting with avoidance, moving to diversion, and then getting aggressive. Sometimes you may use many strategies from all three groups in the space of just minutes! This is most likely to occur when you believe you aren't getting what you deserve, you are stressed out and feel cornered, or when you fear going into the zero state.

Identifying Your Pattern of
Criminal and Addictive Tactics

➤ Which category of tactics—avoidance, diversion, or aggression strategies—do you use first?

_____

➤ Which tactics in that category are your favorites?

1. _____

2. _____

3. _____

➤ When that type of tactic doesn't work for you, which of the other two categories do you switch to first?

_____

➤ What are your favorite tactics in this second category?

1. _____

2. _____

3. _____

➤ Are the tactics you used on the outside the same as what you tend to use on the inside? Why or why not?

_____

_____

_____

■

By understanding your use of criminal and addictive tactics and the thinking behind each of them, you can better understand and begin to change your criminal, irresponsible, and antisocial behavior. Now you are ready to start filling out the Tactics part on your Thinking Report on page 49.

Conclusion

Congratulations. By completing this workbook, you've learned that it is possible to change your thinking. This is good news. You now recognize that you have your own personal mental map that will give you direction and guide your behavior. Your personal mental map helps guide you through life.

This workbook has helped you learn how to think about your thinking. You've learned how to replace old patterns of thinking. A happier, healthier, more free way of life awaits you. And only you can make that happen.

Andrews, D. A., and James Bonta. *The Psychology of Criminal Conduct.* 2d ed. Cincinnati, Ohio: Anderson Publishing Co., 1998.

Beck, Aaron. *Prisoners of Hate: The Cognitive Basis of Anger, Hostility, and Violence.* New York: HarperCollins, 1999.

Beck, Aaron, Arthur Freeman, and Associates. *Cognitive Therapy of Personality Disorders.* New York: The Guilford Press, 1990.

Beck, Judith. *Cognitive Therapy: Basics and Beyond.* New York: The Guilford Press, 1995.

Burns, David D. *Feeling Good: The New Mood Therapy.* Revised. New York: Avon Books, Inc., 1999.

———. *The Feeling Good Handbook.* Revised. New York: Penguin Putman, Inc., 1999.

Greenberger, Dennis. *Mind Over Mood: Change How You Feel by Changing the Way You Think.* New York: The Guilford Press, 1995.

Jones, Dan. *Words for Our Feelings.* Austin, Tex.: Mandala, 1992.

Millon, Theodore, and Erik Siminsen, Morten Birket-Smith, Roger D. Davis, eds. *Psychopathy: Antisocial, Criminal, and Violent Behavior.* New York: The Guilford Press, 1998.

Nakken, Craig. *The Addictive Personality: Understanding the Addictive Process and Compulsive Behavior.* Center City, Minn.: Hazelden Publishing, 1996.

Samenow, Stanton E. *Inside the Criminal Mind.* New York: Times Books, 1984.

Twerski, Abraham J. *Addictive Thinking: Understanding Self-Deception.* 2d ed. Center City, Minn.: Hazelden Publishing, 1997.

Yochelson, Samuel, and Stanton E. Sameow. *The Criminal Personality: A Profile for Change.* Vol. 1. Northvale, N.J.: Jason Aronson, 1976.

———. *The Criminal Personality: The Change Process.* Vol. 2. Northvale, N.J.: Jason Aronson, 1977.

———. *The Criminal Personality: The Drug User.* Vol. 3. Northvale, N.J.: Jason Aronson, 1986.

REFERENCES

A NEW DIRECTION

A Cognitive-Behavioral Treatment Curriculum

Thinking Report

1. Event _____
   _____

2. Thoughts _____
   _____

3. Feelings _____
   _____

4. Behavior _____
   _____

5. Can you identify a core belief? _____
   _____

6. Alternative thoughts _____
   _____

7. Alternative behavior _____
   _____

Thinking distortions _____

Thinking patterns _____

Tactics _____

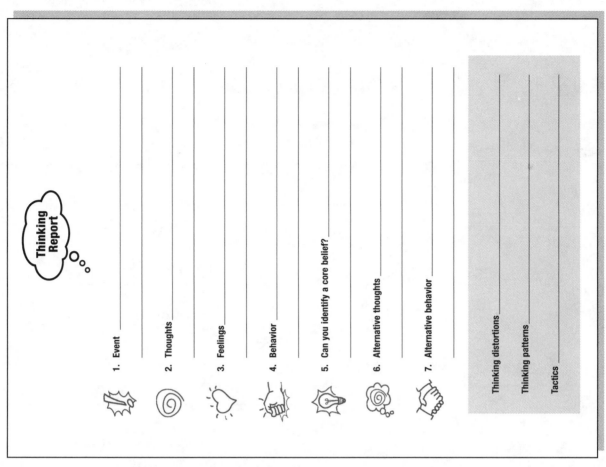

Thinking Report

1. Event _____

2. Thoughts _____

3. Feelings _____

4. Behavior _____

5. Can you identify a core belief? _____

6. Alternative thoughts _____

7. Alternative behavior _____

Thinking distortions _____

Thinking patterns _____

Tactics _____

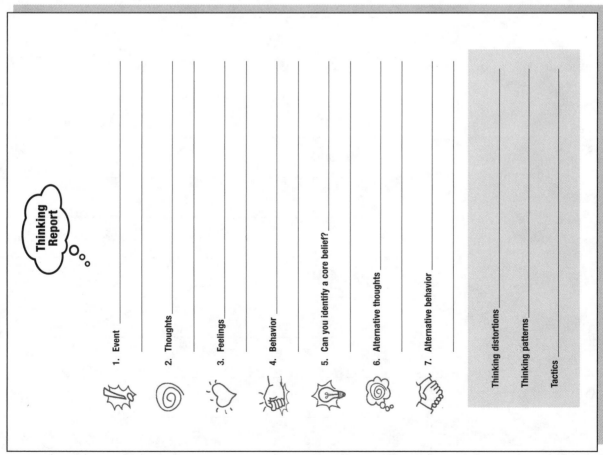

Thinking Report

1. Event _____

2. Thoughts _____

3. Feelings _____

4. Behavior _____

5. Can you identify a core belief? _____

6. Alternative thoughts _____

7. Alternative behavior _____

Thinking distortions _____

Thinking patterns _____

Tactics _____

NOTES

NOTES

NOTES

NOTES